Polynomials, Power Series, and Calculus

THE UNIVERSITY SERIES IN UNDERGRADUATE MATHEMATICS

Editors

John L. Kelley, *University of California*
Paul R. Halmos, *University of Michigan*

PATRICK SUPPES—Introduction to Logic
PAUL R. HALMOS—Finite-Dimensional Vector Spaces, 2nd Ed.
EDWARD J. MCSHANE and TRUMAN A. BOTTS—Real Analysis
JOHN G. KEMENY and J. LAURIE SNELL—Finite Markov Chains
PATRICK SUPPES—Axiomatic Set Theory
PAUL R. HALMOS—Naive Set Theory
JOHN L. KELLEY—Introduction to Modern Algebra
IVAN NIVEN—Calculus: An Introductory Approach, 2nd Ed.
A. SEIDENBERG—Lectures in Projective Geometry
MAYNARD J. MANSFIELD—Introduction to Topology
FRANK M. STEWART—Introduction to Linear Algebra
LEON W. COHEN and GERTRUDE EHRLICH—The Structure of the
Real Number System
ELLIOTT MENDELSON—Introduction to Mathematical Logic
HERMAN MEYER—Precalculus Mathematics
ALBERT G. FADELL—Calculus with Analytic Geometry
JOHN L. KELLEY—Algebra: A Modern Introduction
ANNITA TULLER—A Modern Introduction to Geometries
K. W. GRUENBERG and A. J. WEIR—Linear Geometry
HOWARD LEVI—Polynomials, Power Series, and Calculus

A series of distinguished texts for undergraduate mathematics.
Additional titles will be listed and announced as published.

Polynomials, Power Series, and Calculus

by HOWARD LEVI

Professor of Mathematics
Hunter College of the
City University of New York

D. VAN NOSTRAND COMPANY, INC.

Princeton, New Jersey
Toronto · London · Melbourne

Preface

This book is not intended for use as a text for the calculus course now generally given in the United States, but rather as a text for a proposed replacement for that course.

During the author's career as a teacher of college mathematics, he has seen three courses disappear from the standard college sequence in mathematics in most colleges and universities—college algebra, trigonometry, and analytic geometry. This book is written with the thought that the traditional calculus course is moving toward the same fate. Each year many mathematics departments change their calculus textbook because the old one proved unsatisfactory, only to find that the "new" one leads to a similar sense of defeat. The whole situation, in the author's opinion, suggests that the course itself is at fault and that no text can be satisfactory for it.

The traditional calculus course seeks to impart mastery of the concepts of limit, derivative, and integral. In principle, this is a fine program, but in practice, it seems to be getting out of hand. This could be due to the fact that, whether he knows it or not, the student of calculus is studying a class of functions with some very, very pathological members, and his methodology has been elaborated in order to cope with them (for instance, Riemann introduced his integral in order to investigate highly discontinuous functions). If these difficulties were the necessary price for achieving the benefits of calculus, the teacher could simply apologize and proceed.

The present author believes, on the contrary, that the actual benefit of the calculus is not the mastery of these concepts but the acquisition of skill in dealing with relatively well-behaved functions. He offers a more direct way of acquiring this skill and believes that nothing essential is lost thereby.

The course for which this text has been written has been laid out so that, with a little briefing on nomenclature, the student who wants to go on can reenter the usual sequence where functions of several variables are introduced, with at least as adequate a background as that of

v

the students who have followed the sequence all along. The student for whom this is a terminal course will have learned

how to formulate problems in terms of functions;

how to find unknown functions by solving differential and other types of functional equations;

how to find realistic approximations to these functions; and

how to deduce other properties of these functions from their power series representations.

This new course in analysis covers the calculus of functions of one variable but has a mathematical base that differs from the traditional one. Specifically, it builds around the notion of best approximating polynomials, deemphasizes limits of functions, and omits the Riemann integral altogether (obtaining all its usual applications in other ways).

A major source of the current difficulty with calculus is the need to make simultaneous provision for the divergent professional needs of two broad groups of students: the future scientists (physical, biological and social) and engineers; and the much smaller group of future mathematicians and theoretical physicists. His hope that this book will help solve the problem is based on the following observations.

(1) The large group of future users of mathematics needs to be able to handle only the relatively simple class of piece-wise analytic functions; they do not need to master subtleties appropriate to the far more complicated functions that the pure mathematician will encounter.

(2) The approach to analytic functions presented here is mathematically sound, is an appropriate way to deal with these functions, and is easier to master than the usual approach to the wider class of functions currently treated.

(3) The future mathematician can profitably begin his study of analysis this way. Even though it differs from the standard approach, it gives a sound preparation for a modern advanced calculus course, omitting nothing essential and introducing nothing that needs to be unlearned.

(4) In this development, theory and practice are interconnected so that they reinforce one another; in particular, proofs do not enter as irrelevant niceties, but, in many cases, involve computations that the student will continue to make as long as he uses mathematics.

Most of all, the author wishes to state that he has taught the course set forth here, that he has been pleased with the results and that he hopes that some of his readers will be pleased, too.

——HOWARD LEVI

Contents

CHAPTER 1

Background Material

Much of the material of this chapter will be familiar to many readers. Its purpose is, primarily, to call attention to those portions of secondary school mathematics which will be especially needed in this book and to formulate them in the way they will actually be used.

Order and Absolute Values

Every real number a is associated with a nonnegative real number called the *absolute value* of a, denoted by $|a|$, and defined by these rules:

(1) If $a \geq 0$, then $|a| = a$.
(2) If $a < 0$, then $|a| = -a$.

From this it can be seen that $|-a| = |a|$ for every a, and $|ab| = |a||b|$ for every a and b.

Examples: $|100| = 100$, $|-100| = 100$, $|0| = 0$.

The number is said to be *between* a and b if either $a \leq r \leq b$ or $b \leq r \leq a$, and r is *strictly between* a and b if either $a < r < b$ or $b < r < a$. If a, b, and c are distinct, exactly one of them is strictly between the other two.

Examples: 6 is strictly between 7 and 5, 5 is strictly between 6 and -7, 8 is between 3 and 8, but 8 is not strictly between 3 and 8.

If a and b are numbers for which $a < b$, then the set of numbers x for which $a < x < b$ is the *open interval* (a, b), and the set of numbers x for which $a \leq x \leq b$ is the *closed interval* $[a, b]$. This can also be expressed by saying that (a, b) is the set of numbers strictly between a and b and $[a, b]$ is the set of numbers between a and b.

1

It is possible and useful to describe intervals by inequalities involving absolute values. The following theorem shows how this is done.

THEOREM 1-1:   If d is a positive number and if t is a number, then $|x-t| < d$ if and only if x is in the open interval $(t-d, t+d)$.

Proof: If $t-d < x < t+d$, then $t-x < d$ and $x-t < d$. Since one of $t-x$ and $x-t$ must be $|x-t|$, we see that if x is in $(t-d, t+d)$, then $|x-t| < d$. Conversely, if $|x-t| < d$, then $t-x < d$ and $x-t < d$. This is so because whichever of $t-x$ and $x-t$ is not $|x-t|$ is negative, and d is positive. Therefore, if $|x-t| < d$, then x is in $(t-d, t+d)$.

COROLLARY 1-2: x is in (a, b) if and only if $\left| x - \dfrac{a+b}{2} \right| < \dfrac{b-a}{2}$.

COROLLARY 1-3: $|x-t| \leq d$ if and only if x is the closed interval $[t-d, t+d]$.

COROLLARY 1-4: x is in $[a, b]$ if and only if $\left| x - \dfrac{a+b}{2} \right| < \dfrac{b-a}{2}$.

The next theorem on absolute values is basic, and it will be used frequently.

THEOREM 1-5:   (triangle inequality):   If a and b are any numbers, then $|a+b| \leq |a| + |b|$.

Proof: If a and b are zero, the result is clearly valid. Otherwise we infer from $-|a| \leq a \leq |a|$ and $-|b| \leq b \leq |b|$ that $-(|a|+|b|) \leq a+b \leq |a|+|b|$. Now apply Corollary 1-3 using $|a|+|b|$ for d and 0 for t, to obtain $|a+b| \leq |a| + |b|$.

COROLLARY 1-6: $|a+b| \geq |a| - |b|$.

Proof: Apply the triangle inequality to $a+b$ and $-b$ to obtain $|a| \leq |a+b| + |-b|$, replace $|-b|$ by $|b|$ and transpose.

Exercises

1.   Describe each of the following intervals by an inequality of the form $|a-t| < d$ or $|x-t| \leq d$.

(a) $(-2, 2)$ (c) $(4, 5)$ (e) $(-9, -8)$
(b) $[-3, 3]$ (d) $[-8, 9]$ (f) $(0, 10)$
                                             (g) $[-10, 0]$

2. Find the interval determined by each of the following inequalities.
   (a) $|x| < 5$ (c) $|x-1| < 3$ (e) $|x+3| < 2$
   (b) $|x| \leq 4$ (d) $|x-2| \leq 5$ (f) $|x+9| \leq 9$

3. Prove that $|a+b| = |a| + |b|$ under each of the following conditions.
   (a)   if neither a nor b is negative;
   (b)   if neither a nor b is positive;
   (c)   if and only if 0 is not strictly between a and b;
   (d)   if and only if either a is between 0 and b or b is between 0 and a.

4. What conditions on the relative positions of a, b, 0 are equivalent to each of the following?
   (a) $|a+b| < |a| + |b|$
   (b) $|a+b| = |a| - |b|$
   (c) $|a+b| > |a| - |b|$

5. Verify directly that $|a-c| \leq |a-b| + |b-c|$ if
   (a) $a = 1, b = 4, c = 8$ (d) $a = -1, b = 4, c = 8$
   (b) $a = 1, b = 8, c = 4$ (e) $a = -1, b = -4, c = 8$
   (c) $a = 4, b = 1, c = 8$ (f) $a = -1, b = -4, c = -8$

6. (a)   Prove that $|a-c| \leq |a-b| + |b-c|$ for every a, b, c.
   (b)   Prove that $|a-c| = |a-b| + |b-c|$ if and only if b is between a and c.

7. Prove that if $b \neq 0$, if $|a-b| \geq |a|$, and if $|a+b| \geq |a|$, then $|b| \geq 2|a|$

Functions and Function Notation

Although the function concept is surely not new to the reader, we review here some of the facts about functions that will be needed in this course, and our terminology is set forth.

A *function* is a triple of items consisting of a set D, a set R, and a correspondence which assigns exactly one member of R to each member of D. The set D is called the *domain* of the function, and R is the *range*. The member of R paired with any given member a is the *value of the function at a*. The set of all pairs (a, b), where a is a member of D, and b is the value of the function at a, is the *graph* of the function. (Some mathematicians use the single word "function" to mean what we have called "the graph of a function.")

Notation: It is customary to denote functions by individual letters such as f, g, A, ... If f is a function and t is a member of its domain, then $f(t)$ means the value of the function f at t.

Note: The notion of graph just introduced is intended to extend the notion of graph used in elementary mathematics. There, the graph of a function f is the set of all those points whose coordinates (a, b) have the property that $b = f(a)$. Here, we seem to be ignoring the points in favor of their coordinates. Actually, this is only partly the case. In this course the plane will be regarded as the set of all ordered pairs of real numbers (a, b), and these pairs will be regarded as " points."

We shall also use the word " point " as a synonym for " real number." This usage is based on regarding real numbers as points of the " number line." Here too, a more precise usage of words would identify a real number as a coordinate of a point (in some one-dimensional coordinate system) rather than as a point, but no confusion should arise from this standard practice.

Many (but not all) of our functions have for domain and for range a set of numbers. There are certain standard procedures for constructing new functions from such functions, namely,

(a) the *negative* of f, denoted by $-f$;
(b) if no value of f is zero, the *reciprocal* of f, denoted by $1/f$;
(c) the *absolute value* of f, denoted by $|f|$;
(d) the *sum* of f and g, denoted by $f+g$;
(e) the *product* of f and g, denoted by fg;
(f) the *composite* of f with g, denoted by $f \circ g$.

These derived functions are defined by the rules that the value at x (a) of $-f$ is $-f(x)$, (b) of $1/f$ is $1/f(x)$, (c) of $|f|$ is $|f(x)|$, (d) of $f+g$ is $f(x)+g(x)$, (e) of fg is $f(x)g(x)$, (f) of $f \circ g$ is $f(g(x))$.

Exercises

1. If f and g are defined by $f(x) = 2x+1$, $g(x) = x^2+1$ for every real number x, what is the value at -3 of each of the following?

$f+g$	f/g	$\|f\|$
$f-g$	$f \circ g$	$\|f+g\|$
fg	$\|g\|$	$\|f\|+\|g\|$

2. If $f(x) = 2x^2+1$, $g(x) = x+1$, $h(x) = x^2$, which of the following are correct? $f(g+h) = (fg)+(fh)$, $f\circ(g+h) = (f\circ g)+(f\circ h)$, $(g+h)\circ f = (g\circ f)+(h\circ f)$, $(fg)\circ h = f(g\circ h)$, $(fg)\circ h = (f\circ h)(g\circ h)$, $f\circ(gh) = (f\circ g)(f\circ h)$.

3. Sketch the graph of f if $f(x)$ is

(a) $\|x\|$	(f) x	(k) x^{1965}
(b) $\|x+1\|$	(g) x^2	(l) $-x^{1966}$
(c) $\|x\|+1$	(h) $-x^4$	(m) $-x^{1967}$
(d) $1-\|x\|$	(i) $-x^4$	(n) $x\|x\|$
(e) $\|1-\|x\|\,\|$	(j) x^{1066}	(o) $\|x^3\|$

Sequences

Many terms of mathematics, for instance, "function," are also terms of everyday language. Keeping the two uses separate calls for a special effort on the part of someone learning the terms. The term "sequence" also has both an everyday and a mathematical meaning. There is an additional problem here. The definition given below of "sequence" as mathematical term seems so remote from its everyday meaning that the reader might not see any relation between the two. The fact is that even though its language is quite technical the mathematical definition expresses pretty much the everyday meaning of sequence. The reader is urged to try to see this for himself.

DEFINITIONS: A function is an *infinite sequence* if and only if its domain is the set of non-negative integers. The values of such a function are called its *terms*.

Notation: It is customary to denote the terms of an infinite sequence by letters with subscripts according to the convention that a_0, a_1, a_2, $\ldots$ are the respective values of the function at $0, 1, 2, \ldots$. The term a_0 is the *first* term and, in general, a_n is the $(n+1)$-st term.

Examples:
(a) The rule $a_n = 2n$ defines the infinite sequence $0, 2, 4, 6, \ldots$.
(b) The rule $a_n = 1$ defines the infinite sequence $1, 1, 1, \ldots$.
(c) The rule a_n is the $(n+1)$-st prime defines the sequence $2, 3, 5, 7, 11, \ldots$.
(d) The rule $a_n = x^n$ defines the sequence $1, x, x^2, x^3, \ldots$.

To specify an infinite sequence a rule must be given which determines a_n for every n. Often this rule is not given explicitly; instead, enough terms are listed so that the rule becomes (more or less) apparent.

Examples:
   (a)   1, 1/2, 1/3, 1/4, . . . is the infinite sequence for which $a_n = 1/(n+1)$.
   (b)   3, 5, 7, 9, . . . is the infinite sequence for which $a_n = 2n+3$.
   (c)   1, 0, 1, 0, 1, 0, . . . is the infinite sequence for which $a_n = 1$ if n is even and $a_n = 0$ if n is odd.

Sometimes, as a mathematical puzzle, there are listed some terms of a sequence whose formation rule is not obvious. Three examples are given below (one very easy, one moderately difficult, one almost impossible), but hereafter rules will be supplied where needed.

   (a)   3, 1, 4, 1, 5, 9, . . .
   (b)   1, 1, 2, 3, 5, 8, . . .
   (c)   1, 2, 6, 10, 4, 5, 9, 3, 7, 8, 40, . . .

Because infinite sequences are functions, all the rules for operating with functions can be applied to them. They also admit some special operations of their own. A few will be examined now. We simplify the language in this discussion and use the word "sequence" to mean "infinite sequence whose terms are numbers."

DEFINITIONS: If a_0, a_1, a_2, . . . is a sequence, then the sequence a_1-a_0, a_2-a_1, . . . , $a_{n+1}-a_n$, . . . is called its *sequence of first differences.* If b_0, b_1, b_2, . . . is the sequence of first differences of a_0, a_1, a_2, . . . , then b_1-b_0, b_2-b_1, . . . , $b_{n+1}-b_n$, . . . is the *sequence of second differences* of $a_0, a_1, a_2, ...$ In general, if c_0, c_1, c_2, . . . is the sequence of n-th differences of a_0, a_1, a_2, . . . , then c_1-c_0, c_2-c_1, . . . , $c_{n+1}-c_n$ . . . is the *sequence of* $(n+1)$-st *differences* of a_0, a_1, a_2, ... It is sometimes convenient to think of a_0, a_1, a_2, . . . as the *sequence of* 0-th *differences* of itself.

Examples:
   (a)   The sequence 1, 0, 1, 0, 1, 0, . . . has -1, 1, -1, 1, . . . as its sequence of first differences and 2, $-2, 2, -2$, . . . as its sequence of second differences.
   (b)   The sequence 5, 5, 5, . . . has 0, 0, 0, . . . as its sequence of n-th differences, for $n = 1, 2, 3, ...$

Exercises

1. What are the first five terms of the infinite sequence defined by
   (a) $a_n = n^2$ (d) $a_n = (2n)^{n+1}$
   (b) $a_n = 2^n$ (e) $a_n = 1+2+\cdots+n$
   (c) $a_n = 1+(-1)^n$ (f) $a_n = 1^2+2^2+\cdots+n^2$

2. Give some examples of infinite sequences in which a_n is defined in terms of $a_0, \ldots, a_{n-1}$, for $n > 0$.

3. Give some examples of infinite sequences whose terms are constructed from the terms of other infinite sequences.

4. The definition of infinite sequence does not require its terms to be numbers. Give examples of sequences whose terms are (a) polynomials, (b) functions, (c) sets, (d) sentences, (e) objects, (f) infinite sequences, (g) some imaginative item of your own choosing:

5. Find the sequence of first differences of each of the following:
   (a) $1, 1, 1, \ldots$ (d) $1, 0, 2, 0, 3, 0, \ldots$
   (b) $1, 2, 3, \ldots$ (e) $1, 2, 3, 2, 1, 2, 3, 2, 1, \ldots$
   (c) $1, 2, 1, 2, \ldots$

6. For each of the sequences of Exercise 5, find all sequences which have the given sequence as their sequence of first differences.

7. Is there a sequence which is identical
   (a) with its sequence of first differences?
   (b) with its sequence of second differences but not with its sequence of first differences?

8. (a) Show that if the formula for a_n is $p+qn$, where $q \neq 0$, .then the sequence of second differences of $a_0, a_1, a_2, \ldots$ is $0, 0, 0, \ldots$.
   (b) Show that if the formula for a_n is $p+qn+rn^2$, where $r \neq 0$, then the sequence of third differences of $a_0, a_1, a_2, \ldots$ is $0, 0, 0, \ldots$.
   (c) Show that if the formula for a_n is n^{1776}, then the sequence of 1777-th differences of $a_0, a_1, a_2, \ldots$ is $0, 0, 0, \ldots$.

9. ($\sum$ notation) If $a_0, a_1, a_2, \ldots$ is a sequence, if n and m are nonnegative integers with $b \geq m$, then $a_m+a_{m+1}+\cdots+a_n$ can be abbreviated by the symbols $\sum_{i=m}^{n} a_i$. For instance, $2+4+6+8+10$ can be written $\sum_{i=1}^{5} 2i$, and $\sum_{i=0}^{4} (i+1)^2$ means $1^2+2^2+3^2+4^2+5^2$.
   (a) What sum is denoted by each of $\sum_{i=0}^{n} i^3$, $\sum_{i=2}^{8} (3+i)^4$, $\sum_{i=m}^{n} 3^i$, $\sum_{i=10}^{100} (3+4i)$?
   (b) Write in $\sum$ notation each of $1+2+\cdots+n$, $2^2+4^2+\cdots+(2n)^2$, $1+3+5+\cdots+(2n+1)$, $n^2+(n+1)^2+(n+2)^2+\cdots+(n+r)^2$.

Some Polynomial Algebra

Polynomials will be encountered repeatedly in this course, and we need to have some facility in dealing with them. In this section a few basic properties of polynomials are reviewed.

It is assumed that the reader is already familiar with the terms "co-efficient," "exponent," "monomial," "like monomials," and "degree." Most but not all of our polynomials will be polynomials in a single variable, usually x. Their coefficients will be real numbers. The way we shall write polynomials may seem backwards to some readers—we write $3+4x$, $5-7x+x^2$, ... instead of the more customary $4x+3$, x^2-7x+5, ... This is done in anticipation of the work with power series, where this "backwards" order is standard.

We recall some facts about algebraic operations with polynomials. Addition and subtraction are so familiar that no additional comments about them are needed. Multiplication is a little more complicated. It is based on the general principle that a product of sums $(A+B+\cdots+F)$ $(A'+B'+\cdots+C')$ equals the sum of all the products PQ, where P is a term of the first factor and Q is a term of the second. Thus if A is the polynomial $a_0+a_1x+\cdots+a_nx^n$, and if B is the polynomial $b_0+b_1x+\cdots+b_mx^m$, then their product AB is the polynomial $c_0+c_1x+\cdots+c_{m+n}x^{m+n}$, where c_i is the sum of all products a_pb_q with $p+q=i$. This conclusion expresses the result of multiplying each term a_px^p of A by each term b_qx^q of B, rearranging each such product into the form $a_pb_qx^{p+q}$ and, for each i from 0 to $n+m$, combining into a single term all the like monomials $a_pb_qx^{p+q}$, for which $p+q=i$. This single term has, in general, the appearance $(a_0b_i+a_1b_{i-1}+\cdots+a_ib_0)x^i$, but for values of i larger than n or m some of the entries indicated in this expression are not present. Note that the degree of the product PQ is the sum of the degrees of the factors P and Q.

Example: If A is $3+4x-5x^2$ and if B is $1+x-2x^2$, then AB is
$$(3)(1)+((3)(1)+(4)(1))x+((3)(-2)+(4)(1)$$
$$+(-5)(1))x^2+((4)(-2)+(-5)(1))x^3+(-5)(-2)x^4$$

which equals

$$3+7x-7x^2-10x^3+10x^4.$$

The polynomial $(x+y)^n$ and simple variants of it, such as $(x-t)^5$,

$(3+(x-3))^7, \ldots$, occur frequently in our work. The binomial theorem expresses this product of sums as a sum of products. We recall this theorem now. Later, a version of this theorem will appear in which the exponent n is not required to be a positive integer, as it is here.

DEFINITION: If n is any positive integer, the expression $n!$ (read "n factorial") means the product $n(n-1)(n-2) \ldots 3 \cdot 2 \cdot 1$. The expression $0!$ is defined to mean the number 1.

Examples: $1! = 1,\ 2! = 2,\ 3! = 6,\ 4! = 24, \dfrac{5!}{3!} = 20, \dfrac{7!}{8!} = \dfrac{1}{8}$,

$\dfrac{7!}{3!4!} = 35, \dfrac{3!+4!}{(3+4)!} = \dfrac{1}{168}, \dfrac{(n+1)!}{n!} = n + 1.$

DEFINITION: If m and n are any nonnegative integers for which $m \geq n$, then

$$\binom{m}{n} = \frac{m!}{n!(m-n)!}.$$

The expression $\binom{m}{n}$ is read "m over n" and is called a *binomial coefficient*.

Examples: $\binom{5}{3} = \dfrac{5!}{3!2!} = 10, \qquad \binom{4}{4} = \dfrac{4!}{4!0!} = 1$

$\binom{17}{15} = \dfrac{17!}{15!2!} = 136, \qquad \binom{17}{2} = \dfrac{17!}{2!15!} = 136.$

THEOREM 1-6: (Binomial Theorem): If n is any nonnegative integer, then

$$(x+y)^n = \sum_{i=0}^{n} \binom{n}{i} x^{n-i} y^i.$$

Note: In this statement it is understood that $x^0 = 1,\ y^0 = 1,\ (x+y)^0 = 1.$

Proof: By mathematical induction. The theorem clearly holds for $n = 0$. We show that if it holds for n it holds for $n+1$. We have

$$(x+y)^{n+1} = (x+y)(x+y)^n.$$

Since the theorem holds for n, this equals

$$(x+y) \sum_{i=0}^{n} \binom{n}{i} x^{n-i} y^i,$$

which, in turn, equals

$$\sum_{i=0}^{n} \binom{n}{i} x^{n-i+1} y^i + \sum_{i=0}^{n} \binom{n}{i} x^{n-i} y^{i+1}.$$

Observe that each of these two expressions is a sum of terms $a x^p y^q$, where a is a binomial coefficient and where $p+q = n+1$. The term

$$\binom{n}{0} x^{n+1} = x^{n+1}$$

occurs in the first expression, corresponding to $i = 0$, and no term free of y occurs in the second. The term $\binom{n}{n} y^{n+1} = y^{n+1}$, corresponding to $i = n$, occurs in the second expression, and no term free of x occurs in the first. Each other product $x^p x^q$ with $p+q = n+1$ occurs in both expressions, in the first with coefficient $\binom{n}{q}$ and in the second with co-efficient $\binom{n}{q-1}$. Thus the total coefficient of $x^p y^q$ in $(x+y)^{n+1}$ is 1 if $p = n+1$, $q = 0$; it is 1 if $p = 0$, $q = n+1$; and it is $\binom{n}{q} + \binom{n}{q-1}$ for the remaining pairs p, q with $p+q = n+1$. A straightforward calculation shows that this latter sum is precisely $\binom{n+1}{q}$. This verifies that all the coefficients occurring in $(x+y)^{n+1}$ have the values called for by the binomial theorem, and thus the proof is complete.

In elementary school we learn to respond to the instruction "divide 215 by 11" by writing

$$
\begin{array}{r}
19 \\
11\overline{)215} \\
11 \\
\hline
105 \\
99 \\
\hline
6
\end{array}
$$

Not everyone realizes that this activity permits us to conclude that $215 = 19 \cdot 11 + 6$. Very few know as a result of formal proof (a) that with given integers such as 215 and 11, there exists a unique pair of integers p and q such that $215 = 11p + q$, where $0 \leq q < 11$; (b) that the calculation learned as "long division" can be trusted to yield these numbers p and q. We are going to study a corresponding property of polynomials, and shall prove that the polynomials we seek exist, rather than describe a method for finding them.

THEOREM 1-7: If A is any polynomial and if B is any nonzero polynomial, then there are polynomials P and Q such that $A = PB + Q$, and such that either Q is zero or its degree is less than that of B.

Proof: If A is zero or if its degree is less than that of B, then it is seen from $A = 0 \cdot B + A$ that the theorem holds, with $P = 0$ and $Q = A$. We proceed by mathematical induction on the degree n of A. We have $B = b_0 + b_1 x + \cdots + b_m x^m$, with $b_m \neq 0$ and $A = a_0 + a_1 x + \cdots + a_n x^n$ with $a_n \neq 0$ and $n \geq m$. If the polynomial $(a_n/b_m)x^{n-m}B$ is subtracted from A, the resulting polynomial A' either is 0 or has degree less than that of A. We conclude that $A' = P'B + q$, where P' and Q are polynomials and where either Q is zero or has degree less than that of B. We infer from $A' = A - (a_n/b_m)x^{n-m}B$ that $A = (P' + (a_n/b_m)x^{n-m})B \neq Q$. This is a representation for A of the required type.

COROLLARY 1-8: The polynomials P and Q are unique.

Proof: Suppose there are two representations for A, $PB + Q$ and $P*B + Q*$, of the required type. From $PB + Q = P*B + Q*$ we infer $(P - P*)B = Q* - Q$. If $P - P*$ is not zero, then the left side has degree at least equal to that of B and therefore greater than that of the right side, $Q* - Q$. Since this is a contradiction, we infer that $P - P* = 0$, and therefore $Q* - Q = 0$. We conclude that $P = P*$, $Q = Q*$.

The polynomials A, B, P, Q, which figure in the relation $A = PB + Q$ of the last theorem, have special names. A is the *dividend*, B is the *divisor*, P is the *quotient* and Q is the *remainder*. It is said that A is *divisible* by B and that B is a *factor* of A if and only if the remainder Q is zero.

Exercises

1. Find AB if A is $1 + 2x - 3x^2$ and B is (a) 2, (b) $-3x$, (c) $2 - 3x$, (d) $4x^2$, (e) $2 - 3x + 4x^2$.

2. Find AB if A is $1-x$ and B is   (a) $1+x$, (b) $1+x+x^2$, (c) $1+$ $x+x^2+x^3$, (d) $1+x+x^2+\cdots+x^n$.

3. If A, B, C are polynomials, prove each of the following statements
   - (a) $AB = BA$ (d) $1A = A$
   - (b) $A(BC) = (AB)C$ (e) $A(B+C) = (AB)+(AC)$
   - (c) $0A = 0$ (f) $-A = (-1)A$

4. Given that A and B are polynomials different from zero.
   - (a) Prove that AB is not zero and that its degree is the sum of the degree of A and the degree of B.
   - (b) Prove that the degree of $-A$ is the same as that of A.
   - (c) Relate the degree of $A+B$ to the degrees of A and B.

5. Prove that if A and B are polynomials such that $AB = 0$, then either $A = 0$ or $B = 0$.

6. Prove that if A and B are polynomials, if r is a number, and if $x-r$ is a factor of AB, then either $x-r$ is a factor of A or $x-r$ is a factor of B.

7. Apply the binomial theorem to
   - (a) $(x+y)^5$ (c) $(x-y)^4$ (e) $(3x+2y)^3$
   - (b) $(x+y)^6$ (d) $(x-y)^7$ (f) $(1+a)^4$
   -   (g) $(x^3+y^2)^3$

8. Prove that $\dbinom{n}{0}+\dbinom{n}{1}+\cdots+\dbinom{n}{n} = 2^n$.

9. Prove that $\dbinom{n}{0}-\dbinom{n}{1}+\dbinom{n}{2}+\cdots+(-1)^n\dbinom{n}{n} = 0$.

10. Prove that $\dbinom{n}{q}+\dbinom{n}{q-1} = \dbinom{n+1}{q}$.

11. Prove that if n is a nonnegative integer,
$$(x+y)^n = \sum_{i=0}^{n} \frac{n(n-1)\cdots(n-i+1)x^{n-i}y^i}{i!}$$

12. What does the formula of Exercise 11 suggest for $(1+x)^{-1}$, $(1+x)^{-2}$, $(1+x)^{1/2}$?

13. Prove that if a set has m elements and if r is an integer such that $0 \le r \le m$, then the number of subsets of the set having exactly r elements is $\dbinom{m}{r}$.

14. Find the quotient and remainder if $3+4x+5x^2$ is divided by
    (a) x (e) $5+6x$ (i) $(x-1)^3$
    (b) x^2 (f) $5+6x+7x^2+8x^3$ (j) $(x-1)^4$
    (c) x^3 (g) $x-1$ (k) $(x-1)^{50}$.
    (d) x^{50} (h) $(x-1)^2$

15. Find the quotient and remainder if $3+4(x-1)+5(x-1)^2$ is divided by
    (a) $(x-1)$ (d) $(x-1)^{50}$ (g) x^3
    (b) $(x-1)^2$ (e) x (h) x^{50}
    (c) $(x-1)^3$ (f) x^2 (i) $5+6x$
                                       (j) $5+6(x-1)$

16. Let A and B be polynomials with $B \neq 0$, and consider the set of all polynomials of the form $A-XB$, where X is a polynomial. Show that either the polynomial 0 belongs to the set or there is a single polynomial in this set which is of smaller degree than that of any other polynomial in the set—
    (a) by using Theorem 1-7 of this section and its corollary;
    (b) without using them.
    (c) Show how the conclusions of part (b) of this problem can be used to provide a new proof of the theorem and its corollary.

17. Show that if A and B are nonzero polynomials such that each is a divisor of the other, then there is a nonzero number t such that $A = tB$.

18. Let A and B be polynomials not both zero and let S be the set of all polynomials of the form $XA+YB$, where X and Y are polynomials. Prove
    (a) A and B are in S.
    (b) If D is a nonzero polynomial of S of minimum degree, then D is a factor of every polynomial of S, including A and B.
    (c) If E is any other factor of A and of B (not necessarily a member of S) then E is also a factor of D.

    Note: A polynomial such as D, which is a common factor of A and B which is divisible by every common factor of A and B, is called a *highest common factor* of A and B.

    (d) Show that if D and D' are highest common factors of A and B, then there is a number t such that $D = tD$.

19. (Euclidean Algorithm) $A_1, A_2, A_3, \ldots, A_{r-1}, A_r$ are polynomials such that A_3 is the remainder after division of A_1 by A_2, and in general A_q is the remainder after division of A_{q-2} by A_{q-1}. Moreover, A_r is a factor of A_{r-1}. Prove that A_r is a highest common factor of A_1 and A_2.

20. Use the Euclidean algorithm to find a highest common factor of each of the following pairs of polynomials;

    (a) x^2-1, x^2+2x+1

    (b) $x^2-1, x+2$

    (c) x^2-3x^2+3x+1, x^2-1

21. Almost every fact of this section on the division of polynomials has a version which is valid for positive integers. Exercises 16, 17, 18, 19 also have such versions. Try to find them. Then use the Euclidean algorithm to find the highest common factor of each of the following pairs of integers;

    (a)   26, 8   (c)   81, 6   (e)   25, 1000

    (b)   26, 7   (d)   1000, 25

CHAPTER 2

Polynomials

In this chapter the study of polynomials is continued with the investigation of the functions they define and the development of new algebraic operations on them. Our conclusions will have two aspects—they will supply unformation about polynomials which is useful in its own right, and they will also prepare us for investigating more complicated matters.

Polynomial Functions

If we substitute a number for x in a polynomial in x, the resulting expression denotes a number. It is often convenient to designate a polynomial in x by a name such as $A(x)$, $P(x)$, $f(x)$, etc. Then, if the number t is substituted for x in the polynomial, the resulting number is denoted by $A(t)$, $P(t)$, $f(t)$, etc.

Examples:
(a) If $A(x) = 1+2x-3x^2$, then
     $A(0) = 1$, $A(1) = 0$, $A(10) = -279$, $A(-1) = -4$.
(b) If $f(x) = 17$, then
     $f(0) = 17, f(1) = 17, f(10) = 17, f(-1) = 17$.
(c) If $f(x) = x$, then
     $f(0) = 0, f(1) = 1, f(10) = 10, f(-1) = -1$.

DEFINITIONS: If $A(x)$ is any polynomial, the *function defined* by $A(x)$ is the function which assigns to each real number t the real number $A(t)$. The number $A(t)$ is the *value of the function at t*. A function defined by a polynomial is called a *polynomial function*.

Notation: If $A(x)$, $P(x)$, $f(x)$, etc. are polynomials in x, then the functions they define are denoted by A, P, f, etc.

Our notation gives symbols such as $A(x)$ a double meaning; the value of the function A at x and the polynomial $A(x)$. This should not cause confusion, since the intended meaning is usually clear in each case.

It is possible to substitute another polynomial for x, in a given polynomial. It should be understood that the resulting expression is itself a polynomial. There is also a notation for this kind of substitution. If the polynomial $B(x)$ is substituted for x in the polynomial $A(x)$, the resulting polynomial is denoted by $A(B(x))$.

Examples:

(a) If $A(x) = 3+2x$ and $B(x) = 2+4x$, then

$$A(B(x)) = 7+8x \quad \text{and} \quad B(A(x)) = 14+8x.$$

(b) If $A(x) = 3+2x+x^2$ and $B(x) = 1-x$, then

$$A(B(x)) = 6-4x+x^2 \quad \text{and} \quad B(A(X)) = -2-2x-x^2.$$

From given polynomials $A(x)$, $B(x)$ we can form the new polynomials $A(x)+B(x)$, $A(x) \cdot B(x)$, $A(B(x))$. Notice that the functions defined by these new polynomials can also be constructed directly from the functions A and B and are, in fact, $A+B$, AB, $A \circ B$.

Some of the properties of polynomial functions can be deduced from algebraic properties of polynomials. The next theorem acts as a link between the algebraic and the function theoretic viewpoints.

THEOREM 2-1 (Factor Theorem): Let $A(x)$ be a polynomial and let r be a number. The polynomial $x-r$ is a factor of $A(x)$ if and only if $A(r) = 0$.

Proof: Apply Theorem 1-7 to the pair $A(x)$ as dividend and $x-r$ as divisor to obtain a relation $A(x) = P(x)(x-r)+Q(x)$. Since $Q(x)$ either is zero or has degree less than one, we infer that it is a number, Q, and does not involve x. It is evaluated by substituting r for x, to obtain $A(r) = P(r)(r-r)+Q = Q$. Since $x-r$ is a factor of $A(x)$ if and only if $Q = 0$, the result follows.

COROLLARY 2-2: If $A(x)$ has degree n, then the equation $A(x) = 0$ has at most n solutions.

COROLLARY 2-3 (Identity Theorem): Let $A(x)$ and $B(x)$ be polynomials of degree at most n. If $A(x)$ and $B(x)$ have the same value at $n+1$ distinct points, then, for every x, $A(x) = B(x)$ and the functions A and B are the same.

Proof: Apply the last corollary to show that the polynomial $A(x) - B(x)$ has no degree and must be the zero polynomial.

Note: In certain other courses and contexts polynomials are considered whose coefficients are not required to be real numbers. It is possible for two such polynomials to be unequal and yet to define the same function. This cannot be the case here.

The next theorem shows a somewhat surprising aspect of polynomial functions. It says, in effect, that if any finite list of distinct numbers is drawn up, and if a number is assigned to each entry of this list in any way whatsoever, then there is a polynomial formula for those assignments.

THEOREM 2-4: (Lagrange Interpolation Theorem): Let n be any positive integer, let $x_1, x_2, \ldots, x_n, x_{n+1}$ be any distinct real numbers, and let $y_1, y_2, \ldots, y_n, y_{n+1}$ be any real numbers, not necessarily distinct. Then there is one and only one polynomial $A(x)$, of degree at most n, such that $A(x_1) = y_1$, $A(x_2) = y_2$, $\ldots$, $A(x_n) = y_n$, $A(x_{n+1}) = y_{n+1}$.

Proof: It follows from the Identity Theorem that there could not be more than one polynomial fulfilling the stated conditions. We show now that there is at least one such polynomial by actually exhibiting an algebraic expression which turns out to be the polynomial in question. The expression is

$$\sum_{i=1}^{n+1} y_i \frac{(x-x_1)(x-x_2)\cdots(x-x_{i-1})(x-x_{i+1})\cdots(x-x_{n+1})}{(x_i-x_1)(x_i-x_2)\cdots(x_i-x_{i-1})(x_i-x_{i+1})\cdots(x_i-x_{n+1})}.$$

It is a sum of $n+1$ terms. The i-th term is the product of y_i and an algebraic expression in x which has the value 1 for the value x_i of x, and has the value 0 for each of the other n values $x_1, x_2, \ldots, x_{i-1}, x_{i+1}, \ldots, x_n, x_{n+1}$. Furthermore, this i-th term is a polynomial, which is of degree n if $y_i \neq 0$. Therefore, the sum of all these terms is a polynomial of degree at most n which has the value y_i at x_i for $i = 1, 2, \ldots, n+1$.

Examples:

(a) If $n = 1$, $x_1 = 1$, $x_2 = 2$, $y_1 = 8$, $y_2 = 6$, then the expression is

$$8\frac{(x-2)}{(1-2)} + 6\frac{(x-1)}{(2-1)}$$

which equals the polynomial $10-2x$. Note that this polynomial is of degree one and makes the desired assignment.

(b) If $n = 2$, $x_1 = 0$, $x_2 = 1$, $x_3 = 2$, $y_1 = 1$, $y_2 = 0$, $y_3 = 1$, then the expression is

$$1\frac{(x-1)(x-2)}{(0-1)(0-2)} + 0\frac{(x-0)(x-2)}{(1-0)(1-2)} + 1\frac{(x-0)(x-1)}{(2-0)(2-1)}$$

which equals x^2-2x+1. Note that this polynomial of degree two makes the prescribed assignments.

(c) If $n = 2$, $x_1 = 1$, $x_2 = 2$, $x_3 = 3$, $y_1 = 8$, $y_2 = 6$, $y_3 = 4$, then the expression is

$$8\frac{(x-2)(x-3)}{(1-2)(1-3)} + 6\frac{(x-1)(x-3)}{(2-1)(2-3)} + 4\frac{(x-1)(x-2)}{(3-1)(3-2)}$$

which equals $4(x^2-5x+6)-6(x^2-4x+3)+2(x^2-3x+2)$ or $10-2x$.
It is instructive to compare this example with Example (a).

Exercises

1. If $A(x)$ is $1-2x-3x^2$, what is each of the following?
    (a) $A(0)$ (d) $A(2+x)$ (h) $A(1)+A(x^2)$
    (b) $A(1)$ (e) $A(2x)$ (i) $A(2+3x+x^2)$
    (c) $A(-3)$ (f) $A(x^2)$ (j) $\dfrac{A(x+h)-A(x)}{h}$
                     (g) $A(1+x^2)$

2. If $A(x) = 5-4x+2x^2$, for what numbers t is the value of the function defined by $A(x)$ at t, (a) 11, (b) 5, (c) 0?

3. If $A(x) = 5-4x+3x^2+x^3$, find (a) $A(1+x)$, (b) $A(1-x)$, (c) $A(x-3)$, (d) $A(x^2)$, (e) $A(3x^4)$.

4. Find all polynomials $A(x)$ for which (a) $A(2x) = A(x)+A(x)$, (b) $A(x^2) = A(x)A(x)$, $A(x+3) = A(x)+A(3)$.

5. Prove that if $A(x)$ and $B(x)$ are polynomials of degree n and m, respectively, and if $m \neq 0$, $n \neq 0$, then the degree of $A(B(x))$ and that of $B(A(x))$ is mn. Discuss the cases $m = 0$, $n \neq 0$, $m = 0$, $n = 0$ also.

6. If $A(x) = a + bx$, and if $b \neq 0$, find all polynomials $B(x)$ for which
   (a) $A(B(x)) = x$, (b) $B(A(x)) = x$.

7. Prove that if $A(x) = a + bx$, if $b \neq 0$, then, for every quadruple of real numbers t_1, t_2, t_3, t_4 such that $t_3 \neq t_4$,

$$\frac{A(t_1) - A(t_2)}{A(t_3) - A(t_4)} = \frac{t_1 - t_2}{t_3 - t_4}.$$

8. (Converse of Exercise 7) Prove that if A is a function whose domain is the set of all real numbers and if, for all quadruples of real numbers t_1, t_2, t_3, t_4, with $t_3 \neq t_4$,

$$\frac{A(t_1) - A(t_2)}{A(t_3) - A(t_4)} = \frac{t_1 - t_2}{t_3 - t_4},$$

   then A is a function defined by a polynomial of degree one.

9. If $A(x) = a + bx$, with $b \neq 0$, find all polynomials $B(x)$ such that $A(B(x)) = B(A(x))$.

10. Prove that if $P(x)$ is a polynomial of degree n, then the graph of the function it defines intersects a horizontal line in at most n points.

11. Find a polynomial function f given that
    (a) $f(1) = 2, f(2) = 3$
    (b) $f(1) = 2, f(2) = 3, f(3) = 1$
    (c) $f(1) = 1, f(2) = 3, f(3) = 1, f(4) = 6$
    (d) $f(10) = 3, f(6) = 5, f(2) = 7$
    (e) $f(4) = 3, f(5) = 3, f(6) = 3, f(7) = 0$
    (f) $f(4) = 3, f(5) = 3, f(6) = 3, f(7) = 3$
    (g) $f(7) = 0, f(8) = 0, f(2) = 0$

12. Find a polynomial $A(x)$ if
    (a) $A(1) = 0$
    (b) $A(1) = 0 \ A(2) = 7$
    (c) $A(1) = 0, A(2) = 0, A(3) = 7$
    (d) $A(1) = 0, A(2) = 0, A(3) = 0, A(4) = 7$
    (e) $A(x_1) = 0, A(x_2) = 0, \ldots, A(x_n) = 0, A(x_{n+1}) = 7$

13. (a) What can you say about the polynomial determined by the interpolation theorem if, for some i, $y_i = 0$?
    (b) It is given that $A(x)$ is a polynomial, t is a number and $A(t) = 0$. What can you conclude about $A(x)$?

14. Make up an example for the interpolation theorem in which $n+1$ values are prescribed and the corresponding polynomial has degree less than n.

15. Let $x_1, \ldots, x_{n+1}, y_1, \ldots, y_{n+1}$ be as in the theorem of this section. Show that there are numbers $f_1, \ldots, f_{n+1}$ such that the polynomial

$$f_1 + f_2(x-x_1) + f_3(x-x_1)(x-x_2) + \cdots + f_{n+1}(x-x_1)(x-x_2) \cdots (x-x_n)$$

has the value y_i at x_i for $i = 1, \ldots, n+1$.

Arithmetic Sequences and Polynomial Functions

The material of this section is not needed for the rest of the text, and can be omitted without loss of logical continuity. It is concerned with a connection between polynomial functions and certain types of infinite sequences. It makes contact with the reader's high school mathematics by carrying further the topic of arithmetic progressions. By relating polynomials and infinite sequences it treats two of the major objects of study in this text. However, its value is probably more esthetic than utilitarian, and should be treated accordingly.

The reader has already studied arithmetic progressions. We introduce a class of sequences which include these as a special case.

DEFINITIONS: The sequence $a_0, a_1, a_2, \ldots$ is an *arithmetic sequence of order* 0 if and only if there is a nonzero number c such that $a_n = c$, $n = 0$, 1, 2, ... A sequence $a_0, a_1, a_2, \ldots$ is an *arithmetic sequence of order* 1 if and only if its sequence of first differences is an arithmetic sequence of order 0. In general, if n is a positive integer, the sequence $a_0, a_1, a_2, \ldots$ is an *arithmetic sequence of order* n if and only if its sequence of n-th differences is an arithmetic sequence of order 0. The special sequence 0, 0, 0, . . . is an arithmetic sequence which does not have an order.

Examples:

(a) 1, 3, 5, . . . , $2n-1$, . . . is an arithmetic sequence of order 1; its sequence of first differences is 2, 2, 2, ...

(b) 1, 4, 9, . . . , n^2, . . . is an arithmetic sequence of order 2; its sequence of first differences is 3, 5, 7, . . . , $2n+1$, . . . and its sequence of second differences is 2, 2, 2, ...

For some of our examples of sequences, the rule which specified their terms was an algebraic formula; for others no such formula was given. Considered now are sequences whose terms are given by a polynomial formula. We show the class of such sequences to be the same as the class of arithmetic sequences.

LEMMA 2-5:   If $P(x)$ is a polynomial of positive degree n, then $P(x+1)-P(x)$ is a polynomial of degree $n-1$.

Proof: Let $P(x)$ be $a_0+a_1x+ \cdots +a_nx^n$, with $a_n \neq 0$ and $n \geq 1$. Then

$P(x+1)-P(x)$

$$= a_1((x+1)-x)+a_2((x+1)^2-x^2)+ \cdots +a_n((x+1)^n-x^n)$$

$$= a_1+a_2(2x+1)+ \cdots +a_n(nx^{n-1}+ \cdots).$$

Since the every nonzero monomial in this expression has degree less than n and since only one, namely, na_nx^{n-1}, has degree $n-1$, our result follows.

THEOREM 2-6:   If $P(x)$ is a polynomial of degree n, then $P(0)$, $P(1)$, $P(2)$, ... is an arithmetic sequence of order n.

Proof: By mathematical induction. If $n = 0$, then $P(x)$ is some non-zero constant a_0 and $P(0)$, $P(1)$, $P(2)$, ... is a_0, a_0, a_0, ... , which is an arithmetic sequence of order 0.

Now assume the theorem valid for n and let $P(x)$ be a polynomial of degree $n+1$. Then, because $P(x+1)-P(x)$ is a polynomial of degree n, the sequence $P(1)-P(0)$, $P(2)-P(1)$, $P(3)-P(2)$, ... is an arithmetic sequence of order n. Since this is the sequence of first differences of $P(0)$, $P(1)$, $P(2)$, ... , we infer that this latter is an arithmetic sequence of order $n+1$.

THEOREM 2-7:   (Converse of Theorem 2-6):   If a_0, a_1, a_2, ... is an arithmetic sequence of order n, then there is a polynomial $P(x)$, of degree n, such that $a_i = P(i)$ for $i = 0$, 1, 2, ...

Proof: By mathematical induction. If $n = 0$, then the sequence is a_0, a_0, a_0, ... , where $a_0 \neq 0$. Since a_0 is a polynomial of degree 0, our conclusion is valid in this case. Now assume the theorem true for n and let a_0, a_1, a_2, ... be an arithmetic sequence of order $n+1$. According to the interpolation theorem, there is a polynomial $P(x)$, of degree at most $n+1$, such that $P(0) = a_0$, $P(1) = a_1$, ... , $P(n+1) = a_{n+1}$. We show that $P(i) = a_i$ also for $i = n+2$, $n+3$, ... Since the sequence of first differences a_1-a_0, a_2-a_1, ... is an arithmetic sequence of order n, according to our induction hypothesis there is a polynomial $Q(x)$, of degree n, such that $Q(0) = a_1 - a_0$, $Q(1) = a_2 - a_1$, ... Therefore, $Q(x)$ and $P(x+1) - P(x)$ have the same values at $0, 1, \ldots, n$. It follows from the Identity Theorem that $P(x+1) - P(x) = Q(x)$ for every x. We infer that $P(i+1) - P(i) = a_{i+1} - a_i$ for $i = n+1, n+2, \ldots$ Since $P(n+1) = a_{n+1}$, we infer that $P(n+2) = a_{n+1} + (a_{n+2} - a_{n+1}) = a_{n+2}$. Similarly, $P(n+3) = a_{n+3}$, $P(n+4) = a_{n+4}$, and $P(n+t) = a_{n+t}$ for every integer t.

CorOLLARY 2-8: If $Q(x)$ is a polynomial of degree r, then there is a polynomial $P(x)$ of degree $r+1$ such that $Q(0) + Q(1) + \cdots + Q(n) = P(n)$, for $n = 0, 1, 2, \ldots$.

Proof: The sequence $Q(0)$, $Q(0) + Q(1)$, $Q(0) + Q(1) + Q(2)$, $\cdots$ has for its sequence of first differences the sequence $Q(1)$, $Q(2)$, $\ldots$, which we know to be an arithmetic sequence of order r. It follows that the first sequence is an arithmetic sequence of order $r+1$, and the result follows the theorem.

According to Corollary 2-8, there should be a polynomial of degree three which is a formula for the sums $1^2 + 2^2 + \cdots + n^2$. One way of finding this formula is to find the polynomial of degree three whose respective values at $0, 1, 2, 3$ are $1, 5, 14, 30$, that is,

$$1 \frac{(x-1)(x-2)(x-3)}{(-1)(-2)(-3)} + 5 \frac{(x)(x-2)(x-3)}{(1)(-1)(-2)}$$

$$+ 14 \frac{(x)(x-1)(x-3)}{(2)(1)(-1)} + 30 \frac{(x)(x-1)(x-2)}{(3)(2)(1)}$$

In a first study of arithmetic progressions it is customary to ask two apparently different questions—"What is the n-th term?" and "What is the sum of the first n terms?" The latter question is now seen to be equivalent to the former, when each is applied to the appropriate sequence.

Exercises

1. Find a formula for $P(0) + P(1) + \cdots + P(n)$ if $P(n)$ is (a) 1, (b) n, (c) n^2, (d) n^3, (e) $1 + 2n + 3n^2$,

(f) $\dfrac{n(n-1)}{2}$,   (g) $\dfrac{n(n-1)(n-2)}{3!}$,   (h) $\dfrac{h(n-1) \cdots (n-r+1)}{r!}$.

2. Let $P_0(x) = 1$ and $P_n(x)$ be

$$\frac{x(x-1) \cdots (x-n+1)}{n!} \qquad \text{for} \qquad n = 1, 2, 3 \ldots.$$

Show that

(a) If $P(x)$ is a polynomial of degree n, then there are numbers $c_0, c_1, c_2 \ldots, c_n$ such that

$$P(x) = c_0 P_0 + c_1 P_1(x) + \cdots + c_n P_n(x).$$

(b) If $P(x) = c_0 P_0 + c_1 P_1(x) + \cdots + c_n P_n(x)$, then

$$P(x+1) - P(x) = c_1 P_0 + c_2 P_1(x) + \cdots + c_n P_{n-1}(x).$$

(c) Suppose $a_0, a_1, a_2, \ldots$ is an arithmetic sequence of order n and $Q(x)$ is a formula for the terms of its sequence of first differences. Use part (b) to derive from $Q(x)$ a formula for the terms of the given sequence.

(d) Solve Exercise 1 using parts (a), (b), (c) of this problem.

3. Let $a_0, a_1, a_2, \ldots$ and $b_0, b_1, b_2, \ldots$ be arithmetic sequences of orders n and m, respectively. Prove that $a_0+b_0, a_1+b_1, a_2+b_2, \ldots$, and $a_0 b_0, a_1 b_1, a_2 b_2, \ldots$ are arithmetic sequences. What can you say about the order of each?

4. Let $a_0, a_1, a_2, \ldots$ be an arithmetic sequence of order n. Prove that each of the following is an arithmetic sequence.

(a) $2a_0, 2a_1, 2a_2, \ldots$
(b) $a_0{}^2, a_1{}^2, a_2{}^2, \ldots$
(c) $a_0{}^3, a_1{}^3, a_2{}^3, \ldots$

What can you say about the order of each?

5. Let $a_0, a_1, a_2, \ldots$ be an arithmetic sequence of order n. Prove that each of the following is an arithmetic sequence.

(a) $a_0, a_2, a_4, \ldots, a_{2n}, \ldots$
(b) $a_0, a_1, a_4, \ldots, a_{n2}, \ldots$
(c) $a_0, a_1, a_8, \ldots, a_{n3}, \ldots$

What can you say about the order of each?

The Algebra of Residues

We need to become acquainted with certain algebraic systems which result from modifying the usual algebra of polynomials. The modifications consist primarily in deleting certain kinds of terms, if and when they arise in the course of algebraic manipulation of polynomials. The algebraic systems obtained in this way turn out to obey most of the usual rules of algebra and also permit us to perform divisions, extractions of roots, and other operations not generally performable in the standard system.

If $P(x)$ is the polynomial $a_0+a_1x+ \cdots +a_nx^n$ and if t is a number, then $P(x)$ has a representation as a polynomial in $x-t$. This representation can be found by rewriting each term a_ix^i of $P(x)$ as $a_i(t+(x-t))^i$, expanding according to the binomial theorem, and collecting like terms.

Example: If $P(x) = 3+4x+5x^2$ and if $t = 1$, then

$$P(x) = 3+4(1+(x-1))+5(1+(x-1))^2 = 12+14(x-1)+5(x-1)^2.$$

DEFINITIONS: If $P(x)$ is a polynomial in x and if t is a number, then the representation $P(x) = b_0+b_1(x-t)+ \cdots +b_r(x-t)^r$ is called the *expansion of $P(x)$ with center t*. The *modulo $(x-t)^{n+1}$ residue* of $P(x)$ is the remainder after $P(x)$ is divided by $(x-t)^{n+1}$. The *modulo $(x-t)^{n+1}$ sum* and *product* of two polynomials is the modulo $(x-t)^{n+1}$ residue of their ordinary sum and product.

Note: In the case $t = 0$, we refer to modulo x^{n+1} residues, sums and products instead of modulo $(x-0)^{n+1}$.

The task of dividing a polynomial by $(x-t)^{n+1}$ and computing the remainder is enormously simplified if the expansion of the polynomial with center t is found first. In fact, if

$$P(x) = a_0+a_1(x-t)+a_2(x-t)^2+ \cdots +a_m(x-t)^m,$$

then the modulo $(x-t)^{n+1}$ residue of $P(x)$ is the polynomial

$$a_0+a_1(x-t)+a_2(x-t)^2+ \cdots +a_n(x-t)^n$$

obtained by suppressing the terms (if any) of $P(x)$ with index larger than n. This observation is based on the fact that if

$$P(x) = a_0+a_1(x-t)+ \cdots +a_n(x-t)^n+Q(x)(x-t)^{n+1},$$

then $Q(x)$ must be the quotient and

$$a_0+a_1(x-t)+ \cdots +a_n(x-t)^n$$

the remainder after dividing $P(x)$ by $(x-t)^{n+1}$. It is used on the proof of the next lemma, which tells how modulo $(x-t)^{n+1}$ residues, sums, and products can be computed readily by using expansions with center t.

LEMMA 2-9: Let $P(x)$ be $a_0+a_1(x-t)+\cdots+a_r(x-t)^r$ and $Q(x)$ be $b_0+b_1(x-t)+\cdots+b_s(x-t)^s$. Then the modulo $(x-t)^{n+1}$ residue of $P(x)$, residue of $Q(x)$, sum of $P(x)$ and $Q(x)$, product of $P(x)$ and $Q(x)$ are, respectively,

$$a_0+a_1(x-t)+\cdots+a_n(x-t)^n,$$

$$b_0+b_1(x-t)+\cdots+b_n(x-t)^n,$$

$$a_0+b_0(a_1+b_1)(x-t)+\cdots+(a_n+b_n)(x-t)^n,$$

$$a_0b_0+(a_1b_0+a_0b_1)(x-t)+\cdots$$

$$+(a_ib_0+a_{i-1}b_1+\cdots+a_0b_i)(x-t)_i+\cdots$$

$$+(a_nb_0+a_{n-1}b_1+\cdots+a_0b_n)(x-t)^n.$$

Proof: In each case the difference between the polynomial and the residue proposed for it is divisible by $(x-t)^{n+1}$. This identifies each of the proposed residues as the remainder, after division by $(x-t)^{n+1}$, of the polynomial in question. The conclusion then follows from the definitions of modulo $(x-t)^{n+1}$ residue, addition, and multiplication.

Examples:

(a) The modulo (x) residue of $6+5x+4x^2+2x^3$ is 6, its modulo (x^2) residue is $6+5x$, its modulo (x^3) residue is $6+5x+4x^2$, its modulo (x^{n+1}) residue, for every n greater than 2 is $6+5x+4x^2+2x^3$.

(b) The modulo $(x-1)$ residue of $6+5(x-1)+4(x-1)^2+2(x-1)^3$ is 6, its modulo $(x-1)^2$ residue is $6+5(x-1)$, its modulo $(x-1)^3$ residue is $6+5(x-1)+4(x-1)^2$, and its modulo $(x-1)^{n+1}$ residue, for every n greater than 2, is $6+5(x-1)+4(x-1)^2+2(x-1)^3$.

(c) The modulo (x^2) product of $4+4x$ and $5+6x$ is $15+38x$.

(d) The modulo $(x-1)^2$ product of the polynomials of the previous example is obtained by representing $3+4x$ as $7+4(x-1)$, representing $5+6x$ as $11+6(x-1)$ and multiplying according to Lemma 2-9 to obtain $77+86(x-1)$.

For each positive integer n we denote by $R_n[x]$ the set of all polynomials $a_0+a_1x+\cdots a_nx^n$. It follows that if t is a number, then the set of all polynomials $b_0+b_1(x-t)+\cdots+b_n(x-t)^n$ is precisely $R_n[x]$.

Corresponding to each choice of a number t, the set $R_n[x]$ becomes an algebraic system with an addition and multiplication operation. Although the addition operation is the same for each of these systems, Examples (c) and (d) above show that the multiplication operation is not. These different algebraic systems turn out to have a richer algebraic structure than the standard polynomial algebra. Our next definitions and theorems introduce us to some of this structure.

DEFINITION: A modulo $(x-t)^{n+1}$ *reciprocal* of an element $A(x)$ of $R_n[x]$ is an element $B(x)$ of $R_n[x]$ such that the modulo $(x-t)^{n+1}$ product of $A(x)$ and $B(x)$ is 1.

Examples:
(a) $1+x$ is a modulo (x^2) reciprocal of $1-x$.
(b) $1+x+\cdots+x^n$ is a modulo (x^{n+1}) reciprocal of $1-x$.
(c) $1+x$ is a modulo $(x-1)^2$ reciprocal of $3/4-(1/4)x$. To see this, represent $1+x$ as $2+(x-1)$, represent $3/4-(1/4)x$ as $1/2-(1/4)(x-1)$, and multiply modulo $(x-1)^2$.

THEOREM 2-10:   Let $A(x)$ be $a_0+a_1(x-t)+\cdots+a_n(x-t)^n$. Then $A(x)$ has exactly one modulo $(x-t)^{n+1}$ reciprocal if $a_0 \neq 0$ and none if $a_0 = 0$.

Proof: Let $B(x)$ be $b_0+b_1(x-t)+\cdots+b_n(x-t)^{n+1}$. Then the modulo $(x-t)^{n+1}$ product of $A(x)$ and $B(x)$ is 1 if and only if

$$a_0 b_0 = 1$$
$$a_0 b_1 + a_1 b_0 = 0$$
$$\vdots \qquad \vdots$$
$$a_0 b_n + \cdots + a_n b_n = 0.$$

This system of equations for $b_0, b_1, \ldots, b_n$ has a unique solution if $a_0 \neq 0$, since the first determines b_0 uniquely, the second b_1, the third b_2, etc. Clearly if $a_0 = 0$, the system has no solution.

COROLLARY 2-11:   If $B(x)$ is the modulo $(x-t)^{n+1}$ reciprocal of $A(x)$, then $A(x)$ is the modulo $(x-t)^{n+1}$ reciprocal of $B(x)$.

COROLLARY 2-12: $b_1 = -a_1/a_0^2$.

Notation: From now on we shall use the terms (t, n) residue, sum, product, reciprocal, instead of the terms modulo $(x-t)^{n+1}$ residue, sum, product, reciprocal. The modulo $(x-t)^{n+1}$ language is standard, but the (t, n) language is less clumsy. However, we should be prepared to meet the standard terminology in other contexts.

Exercises

1. Find the (t, n) residue of $1+2x+3x^2+x^3$ if (t, n) is
    (a) (0, 1),   (c) (1, 1),   (e) (−1, 1),
    (b) (0, 2),   (d) (1, 2),   (f) (−1, 2).

2. Evaluate each of the residues of Exercise 1 at 0, 0.1, 1, 1.1, −1, −1.1 and compare each value with the corresponding value of $1+2x+3x^2+x^3$. How does the accuracy of the residue as an approximation to the polynomial function seem to vary with n, with t, with x?

3. Find the (0, 2) product and the (1, 2) product of $1+x-x^2$ and $1-x+x^2$.

4. Evaluate the product of $1+x-x^2$ and $1-x+x^2$ at 0, 0.1, 1, 1.1 and also evaluate their (0, 2) product and their (1, 2) product for these values. On what does the accuracy of these latter products as approximations to the original products seem to depend?

5. Find the (0, 1) reciprocal and the (−1, 1) reciprocal of $3-4x$.

6. Evaluate $1/(3-4x)$ at 0, 0.1, −1, −1.1 and compare these values with the corresponding values of the (0, 1) and (−1, 1) reciprocals of $3-4x$. What does the accuracy of these latter reciprocals as approximations to the original values seem to depend on?

7. Prove that a polynomial in x has a unique expansion with center t.

8. Prove that the set of all polynomials $b_0+b_1(x-t)+ \cdots +b_n(x-t)^n$ is the same as $R_n[x]$.

9. (a) Prove that the (t, n) sum of two elements of $R_n[x]$ does not depend on t.
    (b) Show that the (0, 1) sum of $1+x+x^2$ and $1+2x+3x^2$ is not the same as their (1, 1) sum.
    (c) Reconcile the apparant contradiction between (a) and (b).

10. (a) Find the $(t, 1)$ residue of x, x^2, x^3, x^n.
    (b) Find the (t, n) residue of x^r if i) $r \leq n$, ii) $r > n$.

11. (a)   Show that the (t, n) reciprocal of x is

$$\frac{1}{t} - \frac{1}{t^2}(x-t) + \frac{1}{t^3}(x-t)^2 + \cdots + \frac{(-1)^n}{t^{n+1}}(x-t)^n.$$

(b)   If $A(x)$ is an element of $R_n[x]$, show that the (t, n) reciprocal of $A(x)$ is the (t, n) residue of

$$\frac{1}{A(t)} - \frac{1}{A(t)^2}(A(x) - A(t)) + \frac{1}{A(t)^3}(A(x) - A(t))^3 + \cdots$$

$$+ \frac{(-1)^n}{A(t)^{n+1}}(A(x) - A(t))^n.$$

Composition, Inverses, and the Extraction of Roots in $R_n[x]$

The material of this section is relatively complicated and should be covered only by relatively dedicated students. It is not necessary for most of what follows, and the few sections which refer to it can be omitted without damaging the logical continuity. On the other hand, it is substantial and interesting and rounds out topics which are essential.

In the ordinary algebra of polynomials, it is possible to substitute a polynomial $B(x)$ for x in the polynomial $A(x)$ and obtain a polynomial $A(B(x))$. This possibility suggests the study of the equation $A(B(x)) = P(x)$, where $P(x)$ is given and either $B(x)$ is given and $A(x)$ is sought or $A(x)$ is given and $B(x)$ is sought. A little reflection should show that such equations cannot be solved in general. In fact, if $A(x)$, $B(x)$, and $P(x)$ are polynomials and if the ordinary polynomial algebra is used, then the degree of $A(B(x))$ is the product of the degree of $A(x)$ and the degree of $B(x)$. If the degree of $P(x)$ is not divisible by that of $B(x)$, there is certainly no $A(x)$ such that $A(B(x)) = P(x)$. When we deal with residues, on the other hand, we shall see that the situation is entirely different. It turns out that these equations can be solved, subject to some minor restrictions. Our study of this topic is based on the following lemma.

LEMMA 2-13:   Let $B(x)$ be $b_0 + b_1(x-t) + \cdots + b_n(x-t)^n$, and let $A(x)$ be $a_0 + a_1(x-b_0) + \cdots + a_n(x-b_0)^n$. If the (t, n) residue of $A(B(x))$ is expanded about center t, then the constant term is a_0, the coefficient of $x-t$ is $a_1 b_1$, and for $i > 1$ the coefficient of $(x-t)^i$ is $a_1 b_i + a_i b_1^i + W_i$, where the sum W_i involves only coefficients of $A(x)$ and $B(x)$ with indices less than i.

Proof:

$$A(B(x)) = a_0 + a_1(b_1(x-t) + \cdots + b_n(x-t)^n) + \cdots$$
$$+ a_n(b_1(x-t + \cdots + b_n(x-t)^n)^n.$$

The only terms containing $(x-t)$ to a given power i come from $a_s(b_1(x-t) + \cdots + b_n(x-t)^n)^s$, for $s = 1, 2, \ldots, i$. The first of these contributes $a_1 b_i(x-t)^i$, the last contributes $a_i b_1{}^i(x-t)^i$, and the ones in between contribute terms of the form $a_s b_{i_1} b_{i_2} \cdots b_{i_s}(x-t)^i$. Since for these terms we must have $i_1 + i_2 + \cdots + i_s = i$, none of these subscripts is as large as i. This is what we were to prove.

COROLLARY 2-14: Let $B(x)$ be $b_0 + b_1(x-t) + \cdots + b_n(x-t)^n$, with $b_1 \neq 0$. Then for every $P(x)$ of $R_n[x]$ there is a unique $A(x)$ of $R_n[x]$ such that the (t, n) residue of $A(B(x))$ is $P(x)$.

Proof: Let $A(x)$ be $a_0 + a_1(x-b_0) + \cdots + a_n(x-b_0)^n$, where $a_0, \ldots, a_n$ are unknowns. The (t, n) residue of $A(B(x))$ will be $p_0 + p_1(x-t) + \cdots + p_n(x-t)^n$ if and only if $a_0 = p_0$, $a_1 b_1 = p_1$, $a_1 b_i + a_i b_1{}^i + W_i = p_i$ for $i = 2, 4, \ldots, n$. These conditions determine $a_0, a_1, \ldots, a_n$ uniquely.

COROLLARY 2.15: Let $A(x)$ be $a_0 + a_1(x-u) + \cdots + a_n(x-u)^n$, with $a_1 \neq 0$. Then for every $P(x)$ of $R_n[x]$ and for every t such that $P(t) = a_0$ there is a unique $B(x)$ of $R_n[x]$ such that $B(t) = u$ and such that the (t, n) residue of $A(B(x))$ is $P(x)$.

Proof: Let $B(x)$ be $u + b_1(x-t) + \cdots + b_n(x-t)^n$, where the b_i are unknowns. The (t, n) residue of $A(B(x))$ will be $p_0 + p_1(x-t) + \cdots + (x-t)^n$ if and only if $a_0 = p_0$, $a_1 b_1 = p_1$, $a_1 b_i + a_i b_1{}^i + W_i = p_i$ for $i = 2, 4, \ldots, n$. These conditions determine $b_1, \ldots, b_n$ uniquely.

DEFINITION: If $A(x)$ and $B(x)$ are elements of $R_n[x]$, we say that $A(x)$ is a (t, n) *inverse* of $B(x)$ if the (t, n) residue of $A(B(x))$ is x.

Examples:
(a) If $A(x) = x + x^2/2$, $B(x) = x - x^2/2$, then
$$A(B(x)) = x - x^2/2 + (1/2)(x - x^2/2)^2$$
$$= x - (1/2)x^3 + (1/8)x^4.$$

The $(0, 2)$ residue of $A(B(x))$ is x and $A(x)$ is a $(0, 2)$ inverse of $B(x)$.

(b)   If $A(x) = (x-1)-(x-1)^2$ and $B(x) = 1+x+x^2$, then

$$A(B(x)) = x+x^2-(x+x^2)^2 = x-2x^3-x^4.$$

The $(0, 2)$ residue of $A(B(x))$ is x and $A(x)$ is an $(0, 2)$ inverse of $B(x)$.

THEOREM 2-16:   If $B(x) = b_0+b_1(x-t)+ \cdots +b_n(x-t)^n$,   with $b_1 \neq 0$, then $B(x)$ has a unique (t, n) inverse.

Proof: Apply Corollary 2-14 using x for $P(x)$.

In the usual algebra of polynomials it is exceptional for a polynomial to have an r-th root which is itself a polynomial. In the algebra of residues it is exceptional for this not to be the case.

DEFINITION: Let r be a positive integer, and let $B(x)$ and $P(x)$ be elements of $R_n[x]$. We say that $B(x)$ is a (t, n) *r-th root of $P(x)$* if and only if the (t, n) residue of $B(x)^r$ is $P(x)$.

Examples:

(a)   Since $(1+x)^2 = 1+2x+x^2$, and since the $(0, 1)$ residue of this expression is $1+2x$, we conclude that $1+x$ is a $(0, 1)$ square root of $1+2x$.

(b)   Since $(1+(1/2)(x-1)-(1/8)(x-1)^2)^2$ is $x-(1/8)(x-1)^3+$ $(1/64)(x-1)^4$, and since the $(1, 2)$ residue of this expression is x, we conclude that $1+(1/2)(x-1)-(1/8)(x-1)^2$ is a $(1, 2)$ square root of x.

THEOREM 2-17:   Let $P(x)$ be an element of $R_n[x]$ and let t be a number such that $P(t)$ is not zero and has an r-th root s. Then $P(x)$ has a unique (t, n) r-th root $s+b_1(x-t)+ \cdots +b_n(x-t)^n$.

Proof: Let $A(x)$ be x^r. Then the expansion of $A(x)$ with center s is $s^r+rs^{r-1}(x-s)+ \cdots +(x-s)^r$. Since it is known that $s^r = P(t)$ and since the coefficient rs^{r-1} of $(x-s)$ is not zero, the conditions of Corollary 2-15 apply. We infer that there is one and only one $B(x)$ such that $B(t) = s$ and such that the (t, n) residue of $A(B(X))$ is $P(x)$. Because $A(x)$ is x^r, we conclude that $B(x)$ is a (t, n) r-th root of $P(x)$.

Exercises

1.   Find $A(x)$ if the (t, n) residue of $A(B(x))$ is $P(x)$, given that (t, n), $B(x)$, $P(x)$ are

(a) $(0, 1)$, $1+2x$, $1+x$
(b) $(0, 2)$, $1+x-x^2$, $1+x+x^2$
(c) $(1, 1)$, $1+2x$, $1+x$
(d) $(1, 2)$, $1+x-x^2$, $1+x+x^2$

2. (a) $A(x)$ is $2+2x$. For which center u does the expansion of $A(x)$ have the form $1+a_1(x-u)$? Determine $B(x)$ so that $B(0) = u$ and the $(0, 1)$ residue of $A(B(x))$ is $1+2x$.

    (b) $A(x)$ is $3+4x$. For which center u does the expansion of $A(x)$ have the form $a_1(x-u)$? Determine $B(x)$ so that $B(0) = u$ and the $(0, 1)$ residue of $A(B(x))$ is x.

    (c) $A(x)$ is $1+x+x^2$. For which centers u does the expansion of $A(x)$ have the form $3+a_1(x-u)+a_2(x-u)^2$? For each determine $B(x)$ so that $B(1) = u$ and the $(1, 2)$ residue of $A(B(x))$ is $3+4(x-1)$.

3. Find the (t, n) inverse of $B(x)$ if (t, n) and $A(B(x))$ are

    (a) $(0, 1)$, $1+2x$ (c) $(0, 2)$, $1+2x$
    (b) $(1, 1)$, $1+2x$ (d) $(0, 2)$, $1+2x+x^2$
                               (e) $(1, 2)$, $1+2x+x^2$

4. Find the (t, n) square root $B(x)$ of x if (t, n) and $B(t)$ are

    (a) $(4, 1)$, 2 (c) $(4, 2)$, 2
    (b) $(4, 1)$, -2 (d) $(4, 2)$, -2
    (e)   use each of these formulas to evaluate $\sqrt{x}$ for $x = 1$, 4, 4.41, 9. Comment on the accuracy of the (t, n) square root of x as an approximation to $\sqrt{x}$.

5. (a)   Show that x^2 has no $(0, n)$ inverse, for $n = 2, 4, \ldots$. What condition in the theorem on the existence of (t, n) inverse is not met for these cases?

    (b)   Show that x has no $(0, n)$ r-th root, for $n = 1, 2, \ldots, r = 2, 3, \ldots$. What condition in the theorem on the existence of (t, n) r-th is not met in these cases?

    (c)   Show that x has no (t, n) square root if $t < 0$, $n = 1, 2, \ldots$. What condition in the theorem on the existence of (t, n) r-th roots is not met in these cases?

    (d)   Show that x has two (t, n) square roots if $t > 0$, $n = 1, 2, \ldots$. Explain how this does not contradict the theorem in the uniqueness of (t, n) r-th roots.

6. The expression $1/(1+2x)^{1/2}$ leads to two elements of $R_n[x]$, the $(0, n)$ reciprocal of the $(0, n)$ square root of $1+2x$ and the $(0, n)$ square root of the $(0, n)$ reciprocal of $1+2x$. Compute each for $n = 1, 2, 3$. Do your answers suggest any general rule? If so which?

7. Let $A(x)$ and $B(x)$ be elements of $R_n[x]$. Prove that if $A(x)$ is the (t, n) inverse of $B(x)$, then $B(x)$ is the $(B(t), n)$ inverse of $A(x)$. [Hint: Let $B_A(x)$ be the $(B(t), n)$ residue of $B(A(x))$. Show that the (t, n) residue of $B_A(B(x))$ is the same as the (t, n) residue of $B(A(B(x)))$. Show that this latter residue is $B(x)$. Infer from this that $B_A(x) = x$.]

CHAPTER 3

Functions Having Polynomial Approximations

In this chapter is begun the study of the functions which will occupy us for the rest of this course. They are considerably more general than polynomial functions, but they all have polynomial approximations. We shall study the whole question of what it means for a function to be an approximation to another function. It will be seen how applying (t, n) operations to approximating polynomials provides useful information about the functions being approximated. This study will lead to a central concept of the calculus—the derivative.

Orders of Magnitude

From now on we suppose that each of the functions dealt with has a set of real numbers as its domain and a set of real numbers as its range. We suppose further that if a number t is in the domain of a function, then there is a positive number d such that the whole open interval $|x-t| < d$ is also in its domain. A way of comparing such functions will be introduced which resembles the comparison of numbers by means of absolute values.

DEFINITIONS: We say that the function f *dominates* the function g *at* t if there is a positive number d such that $|f(x)| \geq |g(x)|$ for every x in the interval $[t-d, t+d]$. We say that f *strictly dominates* g *at* t if f dominates g at t and g does not dominate f at t.

Examples:

(a) Let $f(x)$ be x and $g(x)$ be x^2. Then $|g(x)| = |x| \, |f(x)|$, and if $|x| \le 1$, then $|g(x)| \le |f(x)|$. Therefore f dominates g at 0.

(b) Let $f(x)$ be $2+x$ and $g(x)$ be $(x-1)^2$. If $|x-1| \le 1$, then $|f(x)| \ge 1$ and $|g(x)| \le 1$. Therefore f dominates g at 1.

(c) $|f|$ dominates f at t, where f is any function and t any point in its domain.

(d) If $f(x) = 1+x$ and $g(x) = 1-x$, then neither of f and g dominates the other at 0.

THEOREM 3-1:

(1) If f dominates g at t and g dominates h at t, then f dominates h at t.

(2) If f_1 dominates g_1 at t and f_2 dominates g_2 at t, then $|f_1|+|f_2|$ dominates $|g_1|+|g_2|$ and g_1+g_2 at t.

(3) If f_1 dominates g_1 at t and f_2 dominates g_2 at t, then $f_1 f_2$ dominates $g_1 g_2$ at t.

Proof: Clear from properties of absolute values and definition of domination.

It can happen of two functions that neither dominates the other at some given point. However, for certain pairs of polynomial functions it is possible to infer that one dominates the other by examining some crucial coefficients and exponents. We show how to do this now.

LEMMA 3-2: Let $f(x)$ and $g(x)$ be the nonzero monomials $a(x-t)^m$ and $b(x-t)^n$. Then f dominates g at t if either $m < n$ or $m = n$ and $|a| \ge |b|$.

Proof: $g(x) = (b/a)(x-t)^{n-m} f(x)$. If $n > m$, then $|g(x)| \le |f(x)|$, provided that $|x-t|$ is less than the smaller of $|a/b|$ and 1. If $n = m$ and $|a| \ge |b|$, then $|g(x)| \le |f(x)|$ for every x.

LEMMA 3-3: Let $f(x)$ be the nonzero nomomial $a(x-t)^m$ and $g(x)$ be $b(x-t)^n + b_1(x-t)^{n+1} + \cdots + b_p(x-t)^{n+p}$, with $b \ne 0$. Then

(1) f dominates g at t if either $m < n$ or $m = n$ and $|a| > |b|$.

(2) g dominates f at t if either $n < m$ or $n = m$ and $|b| > |a|$.

Proof:

(1) If $m < n$, then $|f|/(p+1)$ dominates each of the $p+1$ terms of $g(x)$ at t. Therefore $|f|$ dominates g at t, whence so does f. If $m = n$ and

$|a| > |b|$, we have $|f(x)| = |b|\ |x-t|^m + (|a|-|b|)\ |x-t|^m$. Since the first term on the right dominates $b(x-t)^n$ at t and, according to what has just been proved, the second dominates $g(x)-b(x-t)^n$ at t, the conclusion is that f dominates g at t.

(2) It follows from the triangle inequality that

$$|g(x)| \geq |b(x-t)^n| - |g(x)-b(x-t)^n|.$$

It is known from part (1) that $(b/2)(x-t)^n$ dominates $g(x)-b(x-t)^n$ at t. Therefore, for some interval $|x-t| \leq d$,

$$|g(x)| \geq |b(x-t)^n| - |(b/2)(x-t)^n| = |(b/2)(x-t)^n|.$$

We infer that $g(x)$ dominates $(b/2)(x-t)^n$ at t and therefore, if $n > m$, that $g(x)$ dominates $f(x)$ at t as well. If $m = n$ and $|b| > |a|$, we have, from part (1), that $g(x) - b(x-t)^n$ is dominated at t by $(|b|-|a|)(x-t)^n$. Then for some interval $|x-t| \leq d$,

$$|g(x)| \geq |b(x-t)^n| - |(|b|-|a|)(x-t)^n| = |a||x-t|^n,$$

so g dominates f at t.

THEOREM 3-4:   Let $f(x)$ be

$$a(x-t)^m + a_1(x-t)^{m+1} + \cdots + a_p(x-t)^{m+p}$$

and $g(x)$ be

$$b(x-t)^n + b_1(x-t)^{n+1} + \cdots + b_q(x-t)^{n+q},$$

where neither a nor b is 0. Then f dominates g at t if either $m < n$ or $m = n$ and $|a| > |b|$.

Proof: It suffices to exhibit a monomial function which dominates g and is dominated by f at t. According to Lemma 3-3, if $m < n$, then $2b(x-t)^n$ defines such a monomial function, and if $m = n$ and $|a| > |b|$, then $\dfrac{|a|+|b|}{2}(x-t)^n$ does.

The statement "f dominates g" for functions is like the statement "$a > b$" for numbers in that it compares the size of two objects without actually saying how large either of them is. The next definitions introduce a kind of scale for measuring the size of functions.

DEFINITIONS: The function f is *bounded at* t if there is a constant function which dominates f at t. The function f has *order* n *at* t if it is dominated at t by $a(x-t)^n$ for every nonzero a.

Note: If f has order n at t and if $0 \leq j \leq n$, then it is clear that f also has order j at t.

Examples:
(a)   Every function defined by a nonzero nomomial $a(x-t)^n$ is bounded at t. In fact if we choose $d = 1$, $M = |a|$, then $|f(x)| \geq M$ for $|x-t| \geq d$.
(b)   Every polynomial function is bounded at every t. In fact, if

$$P(x) = a_0 + a_1(x-t) + \cdots + a_n(x-t)^n,$$

we can take $d = 1$,

$$M = |a_0| + |a_1| + \cdots + |a_n|.$$

(c)   The function whose value at x is $1/x$, for $x \neq 0$, and whose value at 0 is some number c, is bounded at every value of x other than 0. It is not bounded at 0, no matter what value is chosen for c.

(d)   If $f(x) = (x-1)^3$, then f has order 2 at 1, since, according to Lemma 3-3, $(x-1)^3$ is dominated by every nonzero polynomial $a(x-1)^2$.

(e)   If $f(x) = |x|$, then f has order 0 at 0, since if a_0 is any nonzero number, then $|f| \leq |a_0|$ if $|x-0| \leq |a_0|$. On the other hand, f does not have order 1 at 0 since, for instance, $x/2$ does not dominate f at 0.

Here are some useful facts about functions which have been built up from other functions.

THEOREM 3-5:

(1)   If $f_1, f_2, \ldots, f_r$ all have order n at t, so does $f_1 + f_2 + \cdots + f_r$.
(2)   If f is bounded at t and if g has order n at t, then fg has order n at t.
(3)   If f has order m at t and if g has order n at t, then fg has order $m+n$ at t.

Proof:
(1)   Let $Q(x)$ be any nonzero element of $R_n[x]$. Then each of $f_1, f_2, \ldots, f_r$ is dominated at t by Q/r, so their sum is dominated by $r \left| \dfrac{Q}{r} \right|$, that is, by $|Q|$.

(2)   Let $Q(x)$ be any nonzero element of $R_n[x]$ and let M be a

bound for f at t. Then there is a positive number d such that, if $|x-t| \le d$, both $|f(x)| \le M$ and $|g(x)| \le \left| \dfrac{Q(x)}{M} \right|$. This implies that fg is dominated by Q at t.

(3)   Let $q(x-t)^{n+m}$ be any nonzero element of $R_{n+m}[x]$. Then f is dominated at t by $q(x-t)^m$, g is dominated at t by $(x-t)^n$, so fg is dominated at t by $q(x-t)^{m+n}$.

Exercises

1.   Sketch the graphs of the functions f and g near t if
   (a) f strictly dominates g at t and $f(t) = 0$;
   (b) f strictly dominates g at t and $f(x) \ne 0$;
   (c)   each of the two dominates the other at t;
   (d)   neither of the two dominates the other at t.

2.   Supply the details of the proof of Theorem 3-1, showing auxiliary and final intervals for each part.

3.   (a)   If $A(x) = 3x + 4x^2$ and $B(x) = 3x + 2x^2$, show that A does not dominate B at 0.
   (b)   If $A(x) = 3x + 4x^3$ and $B(x) = 3x + 2x^3$ show that A dominates B at 0.

4.   If $A(x) = a_0 + a_1 x + \cdots + a_n x^n$, and if $B(x) = b_0 + b_1 x + \cdots + b_m x^m$, what condition must be satisfied if neither of A and B dominates the other at 0?

5.   Show that if $f(x) = |x|$ then f has order 0 at 0 but does not have order one at 0. Show that if $t \ge 0$, then f is bounded at t.

Approximation by Polynomials

We all have had occasion to use 0.3 as an approximation to $\frac{1}{3}$, 1.414 as an approximation to $\sqrt{2}$, and 3.14 as an approximation to π. We shall work with polynomial approximations that are very similar to these decimal approximations. Two points involving decimals are especially significant in providing an analogy between polynomial approximation and decimal approximation. One is that calculations are often more convenient with decimals than with other ways of representing numbers. The other point is that it is possible to define a number by exhibiting a sequence of successively more and more accurate decimal approximations of it. For instance, the sequence 0.3, 0.33, 0.333, . . . can be considered to determine the number $\frac{1}{3}$. The corresponding facts with polynomials are (a) that polynomial functions are often more convenient to work with than more general functions and (b) an important way of specifying functions in general is to produce a sequence of more and more accurate polynomial approximations to them. For instance, we shall see that polynomials in the sequence x, $x-x^3/3!$, $x-x^3/3+x^5/5!$, . . . give better and better approximations to sin x and that the sequence itself can be used as a definition of sin x.

If we want to decide which of two numbers a and b is a better approximation to the number c, all that is necessary is to compute $|c-a|$ and $|c-b|$. The smaller of the two comes from the better approximation. With functions, the corresponding question is a little more complicated.

The diagram shows the graphs of three functions, f, g, and h. There are good reasons for asserting that g is a better approximation to f than h, and also that h is a better approximation to f than g. The issue

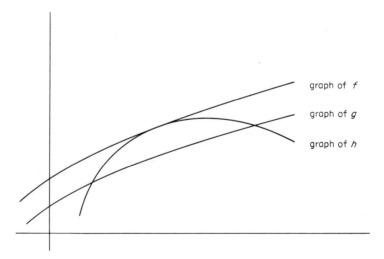

graph of f

graph of g

graph of h

is whether a fairly close approximation over a large range is preferred to a very close approximation over a possibly small range. In some contexts the former is the preferred one, but here we choose the latter.

DEFINITION: A polynomial $P(x)$ of $R_n[x]$ is a (t, n) *approximation* to a function f if $f-P$ has order n at t.

Examples:

(a) If $f(x)$ is $1+2x+3x^2$, then 1 is a $(0, 0)$ approximation to f, $1+2x$ is a $(0, 1)$ approximation to f, $1+2x+3x^2$ is a $(0, n)$ approximation to f for $n = 2, 3, 4, \ldots$.

(b) If $f(x)$ is $1+2x+3x^2$, then 6 is a $(1, 0)$ approximation to f, $6+8(x-1)$ is a $(1, 1)$ approximation to f, and $6+8(x-1)+3(x-1)^2$ is a $(1, n)$ approximation to f for $n = 2, 3, 4, \ldots$. These statements follow from the fact that the expansion of $f(x)$ with center 1 is $6+8(x-1)+3(x-1)^2$.

THEOREM 3-6: A function f has at most one (t, n) approximation.

Proof: Suppose P and Q are (t, n) approximations to f. Then $f-P$ and $f-Q$ have order n at t. Their difference, $P-Q$, also has order n at t. Since no nonzero element of $R_n[x]$ has order n at t, we infer that $P = Q$.

COROLLARY 3-7: If a_0 is the $(t, 0)$ approximation to f, then $a_0 = f(t)$.

Proof: If $|f(x)-a_0| \le e$ for $|x-t| \le d$, then, in particular, we have $|f(t)-a_0| \le e$. If $f(t)-a_0$ were not 0, we could choose $\frac{1}{2}|f(t)-a_0|$ to be e and have the contradiction that $|f(t)-a_0| \le \frac{1}{2}|f(t)-a_0|$.

THEOREM 3-8: If $a_0+a_1(x-t)+ \cdots +a_n(x-t)^n$ is the (t, n) approximation to f, and if $m < n$, then $a_0+a_1(x-t)+ \cdots +a_m(x-t)^m$ is the (t, m) approximation to f.

Proof:

$$f(x)-\sum_{i=0}^{m} a_i(x-t)^i = \left(f(x)-\sum_{i=0}^{n} a_i(x-t)^i\right)+\sum_{i=m+1}^{n} a_i(x-t)^i$$

The first term on the right has order n at t by hypothesis. The second term has order m at t according to Theorem 3-3. Therefore, the right side has order m at t.

COROLLARY 3-9: If $P(x) = \sum_{i=0}^{n} a_i(x-t)^i$ then $\sum_{i=0}^{m} a_i(x-t)^i$ is the (t, m) approximation to P if $m \le n$, and if $m \ge n$, then $P(x)$ is itself the (t, m) approximation to P.

Not every function has a (t, n) approximation for every t and every n.

DEFINITION: A function f is *class $P(t, n)$* if it has a (t, n) approximation.

Note: If f is of class $P(t, n)$, then it is also of class $P(t, m)$ for $m = 0, 1, \ldots, n-1$.

It is shown now that if f and g are of class $P(t, n)$, then so are certain functions derived from them.

LEMMA 3-10: If f is of class $P(t, n)$, it is bounded at t. If it is also known that $f(t) \neq 0$, then $1/f$ is bounded at t.

Proof: Let e be any positive number, and let d be chosen so that $|f(x) - f(t)| \leq e$ if $|x-t| \leq d$. For $|x-t| \leq d$ we then have

$$|f(x)| \leq e + |f(t)|,$$

so f is bounded at t. If $f(t) \neq 0$, choose d' so that

$$|f(x) - f(t)| \leq \tfrac{1}{2}|f(t)|$$

if $|x-t| \leq d'$. Then if $|x-t| \leq d'$, we have $|f(x)| \geq \tfrac{1}{2}|f(t)|$ and $1/|f(x)| \leq 2/|f(t)|$.

THEOREM 3-11: Let f and g be of class $P(t, n)$, and let $F(x)$ and $G(x)$ be their (t, n) approximations. Then

(a) $f+g$ is of class $P(t, n)$ and its (t, n) approximation is $F(x)+G(x)$.

(b) fg is of class $P(t, n)$, and its (t, n) approximation is the (t, n) product of $F(x)$ and $G(x)$.

(c) If $f(t) \neq 0$, then $1/f$ is of class $P(t, n)$ and its (t, n) approximation is the (t, n) reciprocal of $F(x)$.

Proof:

(a) Since $f(x) - F(x)$ and $g(x) - G(x)$ are each of order n at t, so is their sum,

$$f(x) + g(x) - F(x) - G(x).$$

(b) Let $R(x)$ be the (t, n) product of $F(x)$ and $G(x)$. We have

$$f(x)g(x) - R(x) = f(x)(g(x) - G(x))$$
$$+ G(x)(f(x) - F(x))$$
$$+ F(x)(G(x) - R(x)).$$

Theorem 3-5 implies that the first two terms on the right are of order n at t. That $F(x)(G(x) - R(x))$ is of order n at t follows from the definition of (t, n) multiplication and Theorem 3-5. Therefore, $f(x)g(x)-R(x)$, being a sum of three terms of order n at t, is itself of order n at t.

(c)   Let $Q(x)$ be the (t, n) reciprocal of $F(x)$. Then

$$(1/f(x))-Q(x) = \frac{1-Q(x)f(x)}{f(x)}$$

$$= \frac{(1-Q(x)F(x))+Q(x)(f(x)-F(x))}{f(x)}$$

The first term of the numerator is of order n at t by definition of (t, n) reciprocal. Because $Q(x)$ is bounded at t, the second term of the numerator is of order n at t. Thus the whole numerator is of order n at t. Since $1/f$ is bounded at t, we infer that the whole fraction, and hence $(1/f(x))-Q(x))$, is of order n at t.

COROLLARY 3-12:   For every positive integer r the (t, n) approximation to f^r is the (t, n) residue of $F(x)^r$.

COROLLARY 3-13:   Let $P(x)$ be a polynomial. Then $P \circ f$ is of class $P(t, n)$ and its (t, n) approximation is the (t, n) residue of $P(F(x))$.

We have seen, of certain functions built up from other functions, that their (t, n) approximations can be built up from the (t, n) approximations of these other functions. We now examine the case in which the building up process is composition. We assume throughout that $n \geq 1$, since the composition operation is both tricky and trivial for the excluded case, in which $n = 0$.

THEOREM 3-14:   Let g be a function of class $P(t, n)$, with $n \geq 1$, and let f be a function of class $P(g(t), n)$. Then $f \circ g$ is of class $P(t, n)$. If $G(x)$ is the (t, n) approximation to g, and if $F(x)$ is the $(g(t), n)$ approximation to f, then the (t, n) approximation to $f \circ g$ is the (t, n) residue of $F(G(x))$.

Proof: Let $R(x)$ be the (t, n) residue of $F(G(x))$. Then

$$f \circ g - R = (f \circ g - F \circ g) + (F \circ g - F \circ G) + (F \circ G - R).$$

We are to show that this has order n at t. The last term on the right has order n at t because, by definition, it is a polynomial multiple of $(x-t)^{n+1}$. That the second term on the right has order n at t is certified by Corollary 3-13. Examine the first term, recalling that $f(x)-F(x)$ is dominated at $g(t)$ by every nonzero monomial $e(x-g(t))^n$. We show that $f(g(x))-F(g(x))$ is dominated at t by every nonzero function $e(g(x)-g(t))^n$. Choose d so that if x is in $(g(t)-d,\ g(t)+d)$, then $|f(x)-F(x)| \le |x-g(t)|^n$. Choose d' so that if x is in $(t-d',\ t+d')$, then $|g(x)-g(t)| < d$. Then if x is in $(t-d',\ t+d')$, it follows that $g(x)$ is in $(g(t)-d,\ g(t)+d)$ and that $|f(g(x))-F(g(x))| \le e|g(x)-g(t)|^n$. Let $g(t)+a(x-t)$ be the $(t,\ 1)$ approximation to g. Then $e((g(x)-g(t))^n$ is dominated at t by every monomial $eb^n(x-t)^n$ provided $|b| > |a|$. It follows that $f \circ g - F \circ G$ is of order n at t.

CorOLLARY 3-15: If also $f(g(x)) = x$, then $F(x)$ is the $g((t),\ n)$ inverse of $G(x)$.

Exercises

1. If $P(x) = a+bx$ and $Q(x) = c+dx$, find the $(t,\ 1)$ approximation to each of the functions P, Q, $P+Q$, PQ, P/Q, P^r if r is a positive integer, P^r if r is a negative integer. In each case list values of t, if any, for which there is no approximation.

2. (a) Find the $(0,\ 1)$ approximation to the function defined by each of the following expressions:

$$1+x+x^2,\qquad \frac{1}{(1+x+x^2)},\qquad \frac{(1+2x)}{(3+4x)}.$$

   (b) Find their $(-1,\ 1)$ approximations.
   (c) Find their $(1,\ 1)$ approximations.

3. Find the $(t,\ n)$ approximation to the polynomial function defined by $f(x) = x^2$ if $(t,\ n)$ is
   (a) $(0,\ 1)$ (d) $(1,\ 2)$
   (b) $(0,\ 2)$ (e) $(-1,\ 1)$
   (c) $(1,\ 1)$ (f) $(-1,\ 2)$.
   Evaluate each at 0.1, 1.1, -1, 1 and comment on how the accuracy of the approximation depends on t, n, x.

4. (a) Let f be defined by $f(x) = 0$ if $x \le 0$, $f(x) = x$ if $x > 0$. Show that f is of class $P(0,\ 0)$ but not of class $P(0,\ 1)$.
   (b) If $f(x) = 0$, $x \le 0$ and $f(x) = x^n$ if $x > 0$, show that f is of class $P(0,\ n-1)$ but not of class $P(0,\ n)$.

(c)   If $f(x) = |x|$ show that f is of class $P(0, 0)$ but not of class $P(0, 1)$.
(d)   If $f(x) = |x|$ and $t \neq 0$, show that f is of class $P(t, n)$ for every n.

5.   The function f is defined by $f(x) = \sqrt{1+x}$ for $x > 0$.
(a)   Show that if f has a $(0, 1)$ approximation it must be $1 + \frac{1}{2}x$.
(b)   Show that if f has a $(1, 1)$ approximation it must be $\sqrt{2} + (1/2\sqrt{2})$ $(x-1)$.
(c)   Show that if f has a $(t, 1)$ approximation it must be $\sqrt{1+t} + (1/2\sqrt{1+t})(x-t)$.

6.   Show that a polynomial $P(x)$ of $R_n[x]$ is the (t, n) approximation to f if and only if it is the best approximation to f at t, that is, if and only if $f-P$ is strictly dominated by $f-Q$ for every $Q(x)$ of $R_n[x]$ different from $P(x)$.

7.   Show that each of the proposed approximations of Exercise 5 is in fact the approximation in question. [Hint: If $P(x)$ is a proposed approximation, multiply $f(x) - P(x)$ by $(f(x) + P(x))/(f(x) + P(x))$ and deduce from the product that $f(x) - P(x)$ has order 1 at the value in question.]

8.   The function f is defined by $f(x) = 1$ if x is a rational number and $f(x) = 0$ if x is an irrational number. Prove that f is bounded for every t but of class $P(t, 0)$ for no t.

9.   Show that the polynomial $P(x)$ of $R_n[x]$ is the (t, n) approximation to f if and only if
(a) $f-P$ is dominated at t by $f-Q$ for every $Q(x)$ of $R_n[x]$;
(b) $f-P$ is dominated at t by every nonzero polynomial $Q(x)$ of $R_n[x]$;
(c)   there is a function g of class $P(t, 0)$ such that $g(t) = 0$ for which $f(x) = P(x) + (x-t)^n g(x)$ for some interval $|x-t| \leq d$.

10.   Find the $(0, 1)$ approximation to $P(Q(x))$ if
(a) $P(x) = 1+x$, $Q(x) = 2+3x$;
(b) $P(x) = 1+x+x^2$, $Q(x) = 2+3x$;
(c) $P(x) = 1+x+x^2$, $Q(x) = 2+3x+4x^2$.

11.   Same as Exercise 10 for $(1, 1)$ approximation.

12.   Find the (t, n) approximation of $P \circ Q$ if (t, n), $P(x)$, $Q(x)$ are as follows:
(a) $(0, 1)$, x^2, $1+x$ (d) $(1, 1)$, $1+x$, x^2
(b) $(0, 1)$, $1+x$, x^2 (e) $(1, 2)$, $1+x+x^2$, $1-x+x^2$
(c) $(1, 1)$, x^2, $1+x$ (f) $(1, 2)$, x^3, x^3
                                      (g) (t, n), x^r, x^8

13. Let $P(x) = 1+x+x^2$ and $Q(x) = 1+2x+3x^2$. Let $P^*(x)$ be the $(0, 1)$ residue of $P(x)$ and let $Q^*(x)$ be the $(0, 1)$ residue of $Q(x)$. Show that the $(0, 1)$ residue of $P(Q(x))$ is not the same as the $(0, 1)$ residue of $P^*(Q^*(x))$. Does this fact contradict Theorem 3-13?

14. Assume that each of the following expressions defines a function of class $(0, 1)$ and find its $(0, 1)$ approximation.

   (a) $\sqrt{1+x}$ (e) $\sqrt{4+2x+x^2}$

   (b) $\sqrt{1+x+x^2}$ (f) $\sqrt{1+x}/(2+x)^{1/3}$

   (c) $(1+x)^{1/3}$ (g) $(1+x)^{1/3}\sqrt{1+x+x^2}$

   (d) $\sqrt{4+2x}$ (h) $\left(\dfrac{1+x}{1+2x}\right)^{1/3}$

15. Same as Exercise 14 for $(1, 1)$ approximations.

16. If the (t, n) approximation to g is $A(x)$, what is the $(g(t,) n)$ approximation to the inverse of g if (t, n) and $A(x)$ are

   (a) $(0, 1)$, $1+x$ (g) $(0, n)$,

   (b) $(0, 2)$, $1+x$ $1+x+x^2/2!+ \cdots +x^n/n!$

   (c) $(0, 1)$, $1+x+x^2$ (h) $(1, 1)$, x

   (d) $(0, 2)$, $1+x+x^2$ (i) $(1, 2)$, x^2

   (e) $(0, 3)$, $x-x^3/6$ (j) $(1, 3)$, x^2

   (f) $(0, 2)$, $1+x+x^2/2$ (k) $(1, 4)$, x^2

17. If $P(x) = a+bx$ and $Q(x) = c+dx$, state the conditions, if any, for each of the following to have a $(t, 1)$ approximation, and in each case find it subject to these conditions: (a) $P \circ Q$, $Q \circ P$, Q^n if n is a positive integer; (b) Q^n if n is a negative integer; (c) $Q^{1/n}$ if n is a positive integer.

18. The function f is defined for $x > 0$ by the condition $f(x) = \sqrt{x}$ if x is rational and $f(x) = -\sqrt{x}$ if x is irrational. Prove that $f^2(x) = x$. Prove that there is no t such that f is of class $P(t, 0)$. How does this relate to the conjecture that if f is of class $P(g(t), n)$ and if $f \circ g$ is of class $P(t, n)$, then g is of class $P(t, n)$?

Continuous Functions

From now on, the functions with which we deal will be of class $P(t, n)$ for at least one t and at least one n. This section is devoted to functions of class $P(t, 0)$, functions which are traditionally known in mathematics as *continuous* functions. The definition often given for these functions is as follows:

DEFINITION (traditional): A function f is continuous at t if for every positive number e there is a positive number d such that

$$|f(x)-f(t)| \leq e$$

if $|x-t| \leq d$. A function is *continuous* if it is continuous at each t in its domain.

Note: This definition says that f is continuous at t if and only if $f-f(t)$ is of order 0 at t. It follows that f is continuous at t if and only if it is of class $P(t, 0)$. The conclusions of the last two sections imply that all polynomial functions are continuous at every value of t, that the functions derivable from them by forming sums, products, quotients, and compositions are also continuous for all values of t at which they are defined. We shall see later that there are also many continuous functions which cannot be described in this way.

The condition for continuity can be illustrated in terms of graphs. The condition $|x-a| \leq d$ is fulfilled by all points (x, y) in the vertical

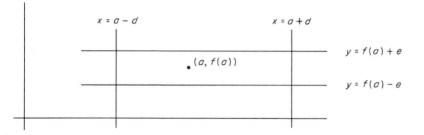

strip bounded by the lines $x = a-d$ and $x = a+d$. The condition $|y-f(a)| \leq e$ is fulfilled by all points (x, y) in the horizontal strip bounded by the lines $y = f(a)+e$ and $y = f(a)-e$.

The condition for continuity of f at a can be thought of in terms of responses to geometric challenges. The challenges are to keep the graph of f near a inside given horizontal strips. The continuity condition says that such challenges can be met by staying inside suitable vertical strips. Consider, for example, the function defined by $f(x) = x$ if $x \leq 2$ and $f(x) = x+1$ if $x > 2$. This function is continuous at every value of x but $x = 2$. At $x = -1$, for instance, to guarantee that $|f(x)-(-1)| \leq e$, it is sufficient to require that $|x+1| \leq e$ if $e \leq 3$ and $|x+1| \leq 3$ if $3 > e$. At $x = 5$, to guarantee that $|f(x)-6| \leq e$, it is sufficient to require that

$|x-5| \leq e$ if $e < 3$ and $|x-5| \leq 1$ if $e \geq 3$. (The choice of 1 for the number d in the latter case is for simplicity. Any number less than 3 would work.) To show that this function is not continuous at 2, select for e the number $\frac{1}{2}$. Then it can be seen from the graph and also from

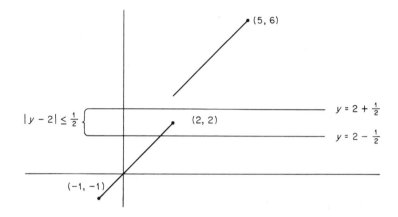

the formulas for $f(x)$ that there is no positive number d such that for $|x-2| \leq d$ we have $|f(x)-2| \leq \frac{1}{2}$. In fact, for every positive number d there is a number t such that $|t-2| \leq d$ and $t > 2$. For this number t we have $f(x) > 3$ and this $|f(t)-2| > \frac{1}{2}$.

Important examples of continuous functions come from extracting r-th roots. If r is a positive integer and if a is a positive number, there is exactly one positive number b such that $b^r = a$. This number is denoted by $a^{1/r}$.

THEOREM 3-16:   Let $f(x)$ be $x^{1/r}$ for $x > 0$. Then f is continuous.

Proof: Let a be a positive number. Then

$$x-a = (x^{1/r})^r - (a^{1/r})^r$$
$$= (x^{1/r}-a^{1/r})((x^{1/r})^{r-1} + \cdots + (a^{1/r})^{r-1}),$$

and so, for $x > 0$,

$$|x-a| \geq |x^{1/r}-a^{1/r}|(a^{1/r})^{r-1}.$$

This implies that $x^{1/r}-a^{1/r}$ is of order 0 at a, whence f is of class $P(a, 0)$.

Continuous functions have a number of important properties which are easy to describe but not easy to establish formally. Chief among these is the following:

FUNDAMENTAL PROPERTY OF CONTINUOUS FUNCTIONS: If f is continuous at each point of a closed interval, then the set of values of f for these points is either a closed interval or consists of a single point. It follows from this property that:

I. If f is continuous for $a \le x \le b$, then f takes on a maximum value B and a minimum value A in that interval.

II. If f is continuous for $a \le x \le b$ and if p is any number between $f(a)$ and $f(b)$, then there is a number c between a and b such that $f(c) = p$. In other words, the continuous function f takes on every value between its values at a and b (and possibly others as well).

This property of continuous functions can be used to illustrate the difficulty of proving these properties formally. Consider the function f defined by $f(x) = x^2$ but consider it only for rational values of x. We have $f(0) = 0$ and $f(2) = 4$. According to Property II, since 2 is between 0 and 4, there should be a number c between 0 and 2 such that $c^2 = 2$. It is well known that there is no such rational number. What conclusion can be reached from these observations? Certainly they do not contradict Property II, because this property was asserted for functions defined for every x between a and b, rational or not. What these observations show is that in order to establish this property we must invoke some special characteristic of the real number system, which is not shared by the system of rational numbers. The usual rules of addition, subtraction, multiplication, division, and order do not come under this heading, since the rules governing these aspects of numbers are the same for the reals and the rationals. Thus there is some less usual fact involved. We state it now, as the "least upper bound property," after some definitions.

DEFINITIONS: A number b is an *upper bound* for a set of numbers S if no number of S is greater than b. A number b is the *least upper bound* for S if (I) it is an upper bound for S and (II) no upper bound for S is less than b. A number b is a *lower bound* for S is no number of S is less than b. A number b is the *greatest lower bound* for S if (I) it is a lower bound for S and (II) no lower bound for S is greater than b. A set S is *bounded* if it has an upper bound and a lower bound.

LEAST UPPER BOUND PROPERTY: If S is a nonempty set of real numbers which has an upper bound, then S has a least upper bound.

Examples:

(a)   The set of positive real numbers whose square is less than 4 is bounded. Its least upper bound is 2; its greatest lower bound is 0.

(b)   The set of all real numbers in whose decimal representation $0.a_0a_1a_2 \ldots a_0 = 2$ and $a_1 = 3$ is bounded. Its least upper bound is $0.24000 \ldots$; its greatest lower bound is $0.23000 \ldots$.

(c)   Let t be a positive number less than 1 and let S be $\{t, t^2, t^3, \ldots\}$. Then the greatest lower bound of S is 0. To see this, note first that since each element of S is positive, 0 is a lower bound for S. Suppose b is its greatest lower bound and suppose $b > 0$. We derive a contradiction. Since $b < b/t$ for some n, we have $t^n < b/t$. Then $t^{n+1} < bt/t = b$. This contradicts the fact that b is a lower bound of S.

Exercises

1.   The function f is defined by $f(x) = 1/x$ for $x > 0$. Show that f has no maximum or minimum value. Show that f is continuous at each point in its domain. Does this fact contradict Property I of the text?

2.   The function f is defined by $f(x) = 1/x$ if $x \neq 0$, $f(0) = c$, where c is some number. Show that, for every choice of c, the function f is not continuous at 0.

3.   State conditions in terms of $|f(x) - f(t)|$ and $|x - t|$ for f not to be continuous at t.

4.   Let S be a set of real numbers and S' be the set of the negatives of elements of S. What relations connect the lower and upper bounds of S with those of S'?

5.   (a)   Prove that the set of positive numbers whose square is less than 2 is a nonempty bounded set. Prove that the square of its least upper bound is 2.

(b)   If t is any positive number and if r is any positive integer, prove that the set of numbers x for which $x^r < t$ has an upper bound. Prove that if b is its least upper bound, then $b^r = t$.

6.   Given that f is continuous at each x in the interval $a < x < b$ and that C is its graph for these values of x.   (a)   Show that if C contains a point above the x-axis it contains infinitely many such points.   (b)   Show that if C contains points which are above the x-axis and points

which are below the x-axis, then C contains at least one point on the x-axis.

7. Show that the function defined by each of the following is continuous (r is a positive integer).

(a) $f(x) = (x+1)^{1/r}$, $\quad x > -1$

(b) $f(x) = (x^2+1)^{1/r}$, $\quad$ every x

(c) $f(x) = (x^2-1)^{1/r}$, $\quad |x| > 1$

(d) $f(x) = (1-x^2)^{1/r}$, $\quad |x| < 1$

(e) $f(x) = 1/x^{1/r}$, $\quad x > 0$

(f) $f(x) = (x^{1/r})^p$, $\quad p$ an integer, $\quad x > 0$

8. Show that if r is an odd integer and a a negative number, then there is exactly one number b such that $b^r = a$. Show that for odd r, if f is defined by $f(x)^r = x$ for every x, then f is continuous.

9. (a) Show that if f and g are continuous at t so are $f+g, f-g, fg, f/g$ (if $g(t) \neq 0$).

   (b) Show that if g is continuous at t and if f is continuous at $g(t)$, then $f \circ g$ is continuous at t.

Derivatives

Functions of class $P(t, 1)$ have proved to be very important in both pure and applied mathematics and have received an enormous amount of study. There is a standard terminology for this class of functions, which is given now.

DEFINITIONS (traditional): Let the function f be defined in some interval containing t. If there is a number b and, for every positive number e, if there is a positive number d, such that

$$\left| \frac{f(x)-f(t)}{x-t} - b \right| \leq e$$

if $0 < |x-t| \leq d$, then f is said to be *differentiable at* t. The *derivative* of f is the function whose value is, at each t at which f is differentiable, the corresponding number b. The function f is *differentiable* if it is differentiable at each t in its domain.

Notation: The derivative of f is denoted by f', and its value at t is denoted by $f'(t)$.

Notes: Observe that f is differentiable at t and that $f'(t) = b$ if and only if f has $(t, 1)$ approximation $f(t) + b(x-t)$. This follows from the observation that the condition given in the definition of differentiability, after clearing fractions, in equivalent to the condition for

$$f(x) - f(t) - b(x-t)$$

to have order 1 at t.

The next theorem is about derivatives of functions which have been constructed from other functions.

THEOREM 3-17:   Let f and g be differentiable at t. Then,

(a) $f+g$ is differentiable at t and

$$(f+g)'(t) = f'(t) + g(t);$$

(b) $f \cdot g$ is differentiable at t and

$$(f \cdot g)'(t) = f(t)g'(t) + f'(t)g(t);$$

(c)   If $g(t) \neq 0$, $1/g$ is differentiable at t and

$$(1/g)'(t) = - g'(t)/g(t)^2;$$

(d)   If $g(t) \neq 0$, then f/g is differentiable at t and

$$(f/g)'(t) = \frac{g(t)f'(t) - f(t)g'(t)}{g(t)^2};$$

(e)   (Chain rule)   If f is differentiable at $g(t)$ then $f \circ g$ is differentiable at t and

$$(f \circ g)'(t) = f'(g(t))g'(t).$$

Proof: The $(t, 1)$ approximations to f and g are $f(t) + f'(t)(x-t)$ and $g(t) + g'(t)(x-t)$.

(a)   The $(t, 1)$ approximation to $f+g$ is the sum

$$f(t) + g(t) + (f'(t) + g'(t))(x-t).$$

(b)   The $(t, 1)$ approximation to $f \cdot g$ is the $(t, 1)$ product

$$f(t)g(t) + (f(t)g'(t) + f'(t)g(t))(x-t).$$

(c)   The $(t, 1)$ approximation to $1/g$ is its $(t, 1)$ reciprocal

$$(1/g(t)) - (g'(t)/g(t)^2)(x-t).$$

(d)   Follows from (b) and (c) by regarding f/g as $f \cdot (1/g)$.

(e)   The $(g(t), 1)$ approximation to f is $f(g(t)) + f'(g(t))(x-g(t))$. According to Theorem 2-14, the $(t, 1)$ approximation to $f \circ g$ is

$$(f(g(t)) + f'(g(t))(g(t) + g'(t)(x-t) - g(t)))$$

which is

$$f(g(t)) + f'(g(t))g'(t)(x-t).$$

Since the function defined by $f(x) = x$ is clearly differentiable, it follows from our last theorem that all polynomial functions are differentiable at every x, and that all quotients of one polynomial function by another, that is, all rational functions are differentiable at every x at which their denominator is not zero.

There is a simple rule for finding the derivative of a polynomial function.

Lemma 3-18:   If $P(x) = x^n$, where n is a nonnegative integer, then $P'(x) = nx^{n-1}$.

Proof: Since $x^n = (t + (x-t))^n = t^n + nt^{n-1}(x-t) + \cdots$, the $(t, 1)$ residue of x^n is $t^n + nt^{n-1}(x-t)$. It follows that $P'(t) = nt^{n-1}$.

Corollary 3-19:   If $P(x) = a_0 + a_1 x + \cdots + a_i x^i + \cdots + a_n x^n$, then $P'(x) = a_1 + \cdots + ia_i x^{i-1} + \cdots + na_n x^{n-1}$.

Proof: The proof follows from Lemma 3-18 and repeated application of parts (a) and (b) of Theorem 3.17.

A more complicated calculation yields the formula for derivatives of r-th roots.

Theorem 3-20:   Let r be a positive integer and left f be the continuous function defined by $f(x) = x^{1/r}$, for $x > 0$. Then f is of class $P(t, n)$, for every positive t and every nonnegative integer n, and its (t, n) approximation is the (t, n) r-th root of x.

Proof: For any such t and n, let $Q(x)$ be the (t, n) r-th root of x.

Then $x - Q(x)^r = (x-t)^{n+1}A(x)$, where $A(x)$ is a polynomial. By direct multiplication we see that $x - Q(x)^r = (x^{1/r} - Q(x))W$, where

$$W = (x^{1/r})^{r-1} + \cdots + (x^{1/r})^m Q(x)^{r-m-1} + \cdots + Q(x)^{r-1}.$$

Since $x^{1/r}$ and $Q(x)$ are continuous at t, so is W. Since the value of W at t is $(t^{1/r})^{r-1} + \cdots + (t^{1/r})^{r-1} + \cdots + (t^{1/r})^{r-1}$, which equals $rt^{(r-1)/r}$, we see that $1/W$ is bounded at t. We have

$$x^{1/r} - Q(x) = (x-t)^{n+1} \frac{A(x)}{W},$$

and since $A(x)$ is also bounded at t, we infer that $x^{1/r} - Q(x)$ has order n at t. It follows that $Q(x)$ is the (t, n) approximation to f.

COROLLARY 3-21:   If $f(x) = x^{1/r}$, then $f'(x) = \frac{1}{r} x^{(1/r)-1}$.

Proof: The $(t, 1)$ r-th root of x is $t^{1/r} + (1/r)t^{(1/r)-1}(x-t)$, and since this is also the $(t, 1)$ approximation of f we see that $f'(t) = (1/r)t^{(1/r)-1}$.

Examples:
(a)   If $P(x) = 1 + 2x + 3x^2$ and $Q(x) = 3 + 5x + 8x^2$, then the derivative of PQ is

$$(1 + 2x + 3x^2)(5 + 16x) + (2 + 6x)(3 + 5x + 8x^2).$$

(b)   If $g(x) = 1/(1 + 2x + 3x^2)$, then

$$g'(x) = -2 + 6x)/(1 + 2x + 3x^2)^2.$$

(c)   If $h(x) = \dfrac{3 + 5x + 8x^2}{1 + 2x + 3x^2}$, then

$$h'(x) = \frac{(1 + 2x + 4x^2)(5 + 16x) - (2 + 6x)(3 + 5x + 8x^2)}{(1 + 2x + 3x^2)^2}$$

(d)   If $h(x) = (1 + 2x + 3x^2)^{1/2}$, then

$$h'(x) = \tfrac{1}{2}(1 + 2x + 3x^2)^{-1/2}(2 + 6x).$$

To see this, regard h as $f \circ g$, where $g(x) = 1 + 2x + 3x^2$, $f(x) = x^{1/2}$, and apply the chain rule.

Exercises

1. If $f(x) = x^n$, derive the formula $f'(x) = nx^{n-1}$ if
   (a) n is a positive integer;
   (b) n is a negative integer and $x \neq 0$;
   (c) n is $1/r$, where r is a positive integer and $x > 0$;
   (d) n is p/q, where p and q are integers and $x > 0$.

2. Find $f'(x)$ if $f(x)$ is

   (a) $2+3x+4x^2$ (e) $\dfrac{2+3x}{4+5x}$

   (b) $1/(2+3x+4x^2)$ (f) $\left(\dfrac{2+3x}{4+5x}\right)^{2/3}$

   (c) $(2+3x+4x^2)^4$ (g) $(3+4x)^{1/2}(4+5x)^{1/3}$
                                   (h) $(3+4x)^{1/2}+(4+5x)^{1/3}$
   (d) $(2+3x+4x)^{1/4}$ (i) $(3+4x)^{1/2}/(4+5x)^{1/3}$

3. If $f(x) = x^{24}$, then $f'(x) = 24x^{23}$. Use this fact to check formulas (b) and (e) of Theorem 3-17 by regarding x^{24} as the product $x^{10}x^{14}$ and as the power $(x^6)^4$.

4. Prove that if the differentiable functions f and g are inverse functions, then $f'(g(x)) = 1/g'(x)$ and $g'(f(x)) = 1/f'(x)$.

5. (a) Prove that if f is a constant function, then f is differentiable and, for every x, $f'(x) = 0$.
   (b) Formulate the converse of this fact, about functions whose derivative is zero for every x. (The converse is true but is not easy to prove at this stage. It will be proved later.)
   (c) Show that if the difference of two functions is constant, then they have the same derivative for every x.
   (d) Formulate the converse of this fact, about functions which have the same derivative (true but not easy to prove at this stage).

6. (a) Find a polynomial function P for which
   $$P'(x) = a_0 + a_1 x + \cdots + a_n x^n.$$
   (b) Show that if Q is a polynomial function for which $Q'(x) = P'(x)$, then, for some number C, $Q(x) = P(x) + C$.

7. (Limits of functions) Let f be a function, let t be a number in its domain, and let L be a number. We say that L is the *limit of f as x approaches t* (in symbols, $\lim\limits_{x \to t} f(x) = L$) if for every positive number e

there is a positive number d such that $0 < |x-t| < d$ implies $|f(x)-L| < e$. For instance,

$$\lim_{x \to z} (x^2-4) = 0; \qquad \lim_{x \to 2} \frac{x^2-4}{x-2} = 4.$$

(a)   Show that f is continuous at t if and only if $\lim_{x \to t} f(x) = f(t)$.

(b)   Show that f is differentiable at t if and only if $\lim_{h \to 0} \dfrac{f(x+h)-f(t)}{h}$ exists.

(c)   Show that if (1) f and g are differentiable at t, (2) for some interval about t, $g(x) \neq g(t)$ if $x \neq t$, (3) $g'(t) \neq 0$, then

$$\lim_{x \to t} \frac{f(x)-f(t)}{g(x)-g(t)} = \frac{f'(t)}{g'(t)}.$$

(d)   (L'Hopital's rule)   Show that if f and g are differentiable at t, if $f(t) = g(t) = 0$, if $g'(t) \neq 0$, then

$$\lim_{x \to t} \frac{f(x)}{g(x)} = \frac{f'(t)}{g'(t)}.$$

(e)   Apply part (d) to

$$\lim_{x \to 0} \frac{2x}{3x}, \qquad \lim_{x \to 1} \frac{x^2-1}{x-1}, \qquad \lim_{x \to 0} \frac{3x+4x^2}{5x+6x^2}, \qquad \lim_{x \to 1} \frac{x^2-3x+2}{x^2-1}.$$

CHAPTER 4

Applications of the Derivative and Antiderivative

Ever since the time of the Babylonians mathematics has been used to describe and investigate the physical world, and more recently it has been used to study biological and social phenomena as well. The invention of calculus led to a major increase in the effectiveness of all such uses of mathematics. One of the " practical " uses of elementary algebra is to help find unknown numbers. The numbers in question are often identified by information expressed in the form of equations, and they are then found by solving the equations. Calculus makes possible a much more ambitious search, in which the unknowns are not numbers but functions. In this chapter we shall glimpse some of these uses of calculus.

Tangents: Maxima and Minima

The $(t, 1)$ approximation to f is a first-degree polynomial

$$f(t)+f'(t)(x-t)$$

which is closer to f near t than any other polynomial $a+b(x-t)$. It is reasonable to expect that the line with equation

$$y=f(t)+f'(t)(x-t)$$

should have some special relation to the graph of f which the other lines $y = a+b(x-t)$ do not have.

DEFINITION: Let f be differentiable at t. The line with equation $y = f(t) + f'(t)(x-t)$ is the *tangent* to the graph of f at t.

The following lemma will help us to distinguish the tangent from the other lines through the point of tangency.

LEMMA 4-1: If f is differentiable at t and if e is any nonzero number, then there is an interval $[t-d, t+d]$ in which $f(x)$ is between $f(t) + (f'(t)-e)(x-t)$ and $f(t) + (f'(t)+e)(x-t)$.

Proof: Since $e(x-t)$ dominates $f(x) - f(t) - f'(t)(x-t)$ at t, there is an interval $[t-d, t+d]$ in which $|f(x) - f(t) - f'(t)(x-t)| \leq |e(x-t)|$. It follows from Theorem 1-1 that $f(x)$ is between

$$f(t) + f'(t)(x-t) - |e(x-t)|$$

and

$$f(t) + f'(t)(x-t) + |e(x-t)|$$

throughout this interval. Since $|e(x-t)|$ is either $e(x-t)$ or $-e(x-t)$, the result follows.

COROLLARY 4-2: Let line q have equation $y = f(t) + (f'(t)+e)(x-t)$ Then for every x in $[t-d, t+d]$ the point $(x, f(x))$ is below q if $e(x-t) > 0$ and above q if $e(x-t) < 0$ (every nontangent line crosses the graph).

COROLLARY 4-3: Let q be a line through $(t, f(t))$ such that, for every x in some interval $[t-d, t+d]$ all the points $(x, f(x))$ of the graph of f are on one side of q. Then q is the tangent to the graph of f at t.

Note: The last corollary says that if a line through $(t, f(t))$ does not cross the graph of f at t, then it must be the tangent line to the graph at $(t, f(t))$. It does not say, nor is it so, that no tangent line crosses the graph at its point of tangency.

Lemma 4-1 and Corollary 4-2 are interpreted in the figure. It shows a shaded region bounded by lines $x = t-d$, $x = t-d$, and two lines through $(t, f(t))$, one with slope $M > f'(t)$ and the other with slope $m < f'(t)$. The results imply that for all values of x in some interval $(t, t+d)$ the

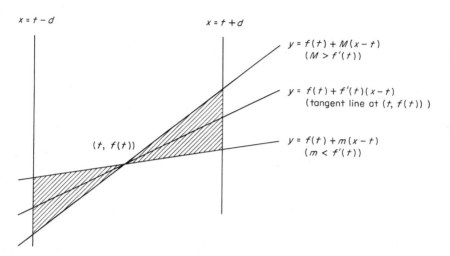

points $(x, f(x))$ of the graph of f lie above the line $y = f(t) + m(x-t)$ and below the line $y = f(t) + M(x-t)$, whereas for all x in $(t-d, t)$ the points $(s, f(x))$ lie below $y = f(t) + m(x-t)$ and above $y = f(t) + M(x-t)$. Thus the points $(x, f(x))$ of the graph corresponding to values of x in the interval $(t-d, t+d)$ lie in the shaded region, and each of the lines $y = f(t) + m(x-t)$ and $y = f(t) + M(x-t)$ cross it. Clearly the points of tangent corresponding to these values of x also must lie in the shaded region.

One of the major applications of calculus is concerned with the study of maximum and minimum values of functions. This application is based on the following definitions and theorem.

DEFINITIONS: The function f has a *relative maximum* at t if there is an interval $|x-t| \leq d$ such that $f(x) \leq f(t)$ for every x in this interval. The function f has a *relative minimum* at t if there is an interval $|x-t| \leq d$ such that $f(x) \geq f(t)$ for every x in this interval.

THEOREM 4-4: If f is of class $P(t, 1)$ and has a relative maximum or minimum at t, then its derivative at t is 0.

Proof: If f has a relative maximum at t, then its graph lies in the lower half plane of the line $y = f(t)$, and if it has a relative minimum, its graph lies in the upper half plane of this line, for some interval $|x-t| \leq d$. In either case it follows from Corollary 4-3 that this line is the tangent to the graph of f at $(t, f(t))$, and since the slope of this line is 0, we infer that $f'(t) = 0$.

This theorem supplies a way of attacking certain problems involving extremes, such as the most efficient design for an object or the most efficient strategy for an enterprise. The problems in question must be translatable into the question, "Which are the relative maximum and minimum points on the graph of the differentiable function f?" The attack in question is to find the points on the graph at which the tangent is horizontal. A limitation of this approach is revealed by the figure, which shows that horizontal tangents can occur at points on the graph

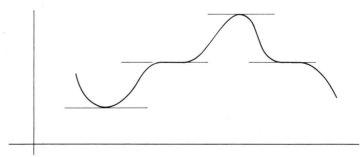

which are relative maxima, relative minima, or neither. The next theorem provides a test for deciding which of these possibilities actually occurs at a given point on the graph of a given function where the tangent is horizontal.

THEOREM 4-5:   Let

$$a_0 + a_r(x-t)^r + a_{r+1}(x-t)^{r+1} + \cdots a_n(x-t)^n$$

be the (t, n) approximation to f, where $r > 1$ and $a_r \neq 0$. Then f has a relative maximum at t if r is even and $a_r < 0$, a relative minimum at t if r is even and $a_r > 0$, and neither a relative maximum or minimum at t if r is odd.

Proof: Since $a_r(x-t)^r$ strictly dominates

$$a_{r+1}(x-t)^{r+1} + \cdots + a_n(x-t)^n,$$

for some positive number d, the sign of $f(x) - a_0$ is the same as the sign of $a_r(x-t)^r$ for $|x-t| \leq d$. It follows immediately that if r is even and a_r is positive, then $a_r(x-t)^r \geq 0$, that if r is even and a_r is negative, then $a_r(x-t)^r \leq 0$, and that if r is odd, then $a_r(x-t)^r$ has both negative and positive values in every interval $|x-t| \leq d$. Since $a_0 = f(t)$, the result follows from the definitions of relative maximum and minimum.

Examples:
(a) Let us find a rectangle of maximum area having perimeter 1. If its length is x, its width is $(1-2x)/2$ and its area is $(1/2)x-x^2$. The derivative of the area function is $1/2-2x$. This is zero if and only if $x = \frac{1}{4}$, or if and only if the rectangle is a square. The $(\frac{1}{4}, 2)$ approximation to the area function is clearly $\frac{1}{16} - (x-\frac{1}{4})^2$, so we can conclude that the area has a relative maximum at $\frac{1}{4}$, since, in the notation of Theorem 4-5, $r = 2$ and $a_2 = -1$.

(b) Let $f(x)$ be $a+bx+cx^2+dx^3$, where $d \neq 0$. Assume that at $x = t$ the tangent to the graph of f is horizontal, but the point of tangency is neither a relative maximum nor a relative minimum. We shall prove that this implies that the graph of f has no relative maximum or minimum points. Denote the $(t, 3)$ residue of $f(x)$ by

$$d_0+d_1(x-t)+d_2(x-t)^2+d_3(x-t)^3.$$

Because the tangent is horizontal at $x = t$, we conclude that $d_1 = 0$. Because this is neither a relative maximum nor minimum, we infer that $d_2 = 0$. The calculations yielding the residue of $f(x)$ show that $d_3 = d$. We infer that $f(x) = f(t)+d(x-t)^3$, whence $f'(x) = 3d(x-t)^2$. Thus there is no value of x other than t at which $f'(x)$ is 0.

Exercises

1. Find an equation for the tangent to the graph of f at the given point.
   (a) $f(x) = x^2$ at $(1, 1)$
   (b) $f(x) = 3+4x^2$ at $(1, 7)$
   (c) $f(x) = 3+4x$ at $(1, 7)$
   (d) $f(x) = 3$ at $(7, 3)$
   (e) $f(x) = \sqrt{4-3x}$ at $(1, 1)$

2. Test for relative maxima and minima the function defined by

(a) $1+2x$	(e) $-3x+2x^3$	(i) $10x+x^2+x^3$
(b) $1+2x+x^2$	(f) $-3+2x^3$	(j) $10x-x^2+x^2$
(c) $1+2x+3x^2$	(g) x^2+x^4	(k) $10x+x^2-x^3$
(d) $-3x^2+2x^3$	(h) $3x+3x^2+x^3$	(l) x^{1588}
		(m) x^{1969}

3. What is the maximum value of the product of two numbers whose sum is 10?

4. What is the minimum value of the sum of the cubes of two numbers whose sum is 10?

5. An open box is to be made by cutting squares off the corners of a rectangle and bending up the sides. Find the maximum volume of the box that can be made in this way from a rectangle which is 6 in. by 10 in.

6. Find the minimum distance from the point (a, b) to the graph whose equation is (a) $y = mx+b$; (b) $x^2+y^2 = 1$. Use derivatives in each case, and also try to verify your answers without using calculus.

7. The tangent to a circle at P is sometimes defined as the line through P which contains no other point of the circle.
   (a) Prove that the circle lies wholly on one side of such a line.
   (b) Does this fact prove that such a line is a tangent line in the sense of this chapter?
   (c) Show that the tangent line to a circle in the sense of high school geometry is also a tangent line in the sense of this chapter.

Some Useful Theorems

It never happens that people discover functions in nature bearing the label, "Find my derivative." Relating calculus to other intellectual enterprises is itself a serious task which needs study of its own. This section is devoted to a few theorems which act as connecting links between mathematical theory and some situations in which it is applied.

THEOREM 4-6:   Let the functions F and f be defined for some interval $|x-t| < d$, and suppose that for every x of this interval there is a w between x and t such that $F(x)-F(t) = (x-t)f(w)$. If f is continuous at t, then F is differentiable at t and $F'(t) = f(t)$.

Proof: We are to show that $F(x)-F(t)-f(t)$ has order one at t. According to the hypothesis this expression equals $(x-t)(f(w)-f(t))$. Let $e(x-t)$ be any nonzero monomial. Because f is continuous at t, there is a q such that $|f(x)-f(t)| \le e$ for every x in the interval $[t-q, t+q]$. The fact that w is between x and t implies that w is in this interval if x

is. We infer that $|(f(w)-f(t))(x-t)| \leq |e(x-t)|$ gor every x in this interval. Therefore, $F(x)-F(t)-f(t)(x-t)$ has order one at t.

COROLLARY 4-7: Let f be continuous throughout the interval (a, b), and suppose for every x and t of this interval that $F(x)-F(t)$ is between $(x-t)f$ and $(x-t)\bar{f}$, where f and $\bar{f}$ are the maximum and minimum values of f in the interval $[x, t]$. Then F is differentiable in the interval $a < x < b$ and $F'(x) = f(x)$.

Proof: It follows from the hypothesis that $F(x)-F(t) = (x-t)q$, where q is between f and $\bar{f}$. It follows from the fundamental property of continuous functions that there is a w between x and t such that $q = f(w)$. Our result then follows from the theorem just proved.

This theorem has two types of applications—it can certify that an unknown function f is the derivative of a known function F, and it can certify that an unknown function F has a known derivative f. In each case this knowledge goes a long way toward finding the unknown function. Knowing that $F' = f$ determines f completely if F is given. To see what this tells us about F if f is given we need to develop this theory further. The next theorem, among its other uses, has a corollary which tells us to what extent a function is determined by its derivative.

THEOREM 4-8 (Mean Value Theorem): Let f be differentiable in the interval I. If a and b are any distinct points of I, there is a c, strictly between them, such that

$$f(b) = f(a) + (b-a)f'(c).$$

Proof: Define an auxiliary function F by

$$F(x) = f(x) - f(a) - (x-a)k,$$

where k is the number which makes $F(b) = 0$. Clearly, F is differentiable in I. Since $F(a) = 0$, then either (1) $F(x) = 0$ for every x in the interval, (2) $F(x)$ has some positive values and hence has a relative maximum at some interior point c, (3) $F(x)$ has some negative values and hence has a relative minimum at some interior point c. In cases (2) and (3) we have $F'(c) = 0$. In case (1), for every x of the interval we have $F'(x) = 0$. Since $F'(x) = f'(x) - k$, we infer that $k = f'(c)$. Thus

$$F(b) = 0 = f(b) - f(a) - (b-a)f'(c)$$

and the result follows.

COROLLARY 4-9   (Rolles's   Theorem):   If $f(a) = f(b) = 0$,   then
$f'(c) = 0$.

COROLLARY 4-10:   If $f'(x) = 0$ for every x in I, then f is a constant
function on I.

Proof: Let a be any point of I. For every x in I there is

$$f(x) = f(a) + (x-a)f'(w),$$

where w is between x and a. Since $f'(w) = 0$, we infer $f(x) = f(a)$ for
every x in I.

COROLLARY 4-11:   If functions f and g have the same derivative at
each x in I, then $f-g$ is constant in I.

Proof: $(f-g)' = f'-g' = 0$.

COROLLARY 4-12:   If f and g have the same derivative at each x in I,
and if $f(a) = 0$, then $f(x) = g(x)-g(a)$ for every x in I.

The next theorem implies that if a differentiable function has a
continuous inverse, then this inverse is also differentiable.

THEOREM 4-13:   Let g be continuous, let f be differentiable, and
suppose that $f(g(x)) = x$. If $f'(g(x)) \neq 0$ for every x in some interval I,
then g is differentiable in I and $g'(x) = 1/f'(g(x))$.

Proof: For every x and t in I we have $f(g(x)) - f(g(t)) = x-t$.
According to the Mean Value Theorem we also have $f(g(x)) - f(g(t)) =$
$f'(c)(g(x) - g(t))$, where c is between $g(x)$ and $g(t)$. Because g is continuous, there is a w between x and t such that $c = g(w)$. We infer
that $x-t = f'(g(w))(g(x) - g(t))$, whence, because $f'(g(w)) \neq 0$ we have
$g(x) - g(t) = \dfrac{1}{f'(g(w))}(x-t)$. Theorem 4-6 tells us that $g'(t) = 1/f'(g(t))$.

If it had been given that g is differentiable, we could have derived
the formula $g'(x) = 1/f'(g(x))$ directly by using the rule for finding the
derivative of composite functions. The point of Theorem 4-13 is that
the differentiability of g does not have to be assumed—it follows from
its continuity. We shall refer to this fact in Chapter 7, where the elementary functions are considered.

The Mean Value Theorem has a simple geometric interpretation, namely, that between any two points A and B of the graph of a differentiable function f there is a point C at which the tangent to the

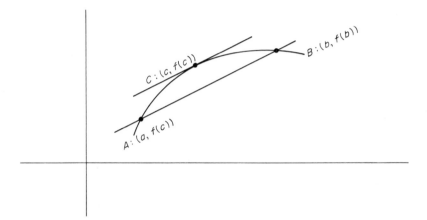

graph is parallel to the line AB. This interpretation is based on the facts that the slope of AB is $\dfrac{f(b)-f(a)}{b-a}$, the slope of the tangent is $f'(c)$, and the equality of the slopes implies the parallelism of the lines.

Corollaries 4-11 and 4-12 are useful in solving problems in which the derivative of a function is known and the function itself is sought.

The following terminology is used in the exercises and in later work.

DEFINITION: If f and g are functions for which $f' = g$, then f is an *antiderivative* of g.

Notation: The integral sign $\int$ is often used to denote antiderivatives: $f = \int g$ means $f' = g$. Often a more elaborate notation is used: $\int g(x)dx$ also denotes a function f for which $f'(x) = g(x)$. Sometimes antiderivatives are called *indefinite integrals*. The word "indefinite" distinguishes them from "definite integrals," whose detailed treatment is beyond the scope of this course. The definite integral is a very elaborate assignment of a number, denoted by $\int_a^b f(x)dx$, to a function f and an interval $[a, b]$ in its domain. For some functions f the assignment process fails (f is not integrable). For some functions f the assigned number exists but cannot be found by any systematic procedure. For the functions f which arise in almost all of the standard applications of calculus, the number in question turns out to be $F(b)-F(a)$, where F is any antiderivative of f. The fact that this number, originally specified in such an elaborate way, can be found in such a simple way, is expressed in a theorem called "The Fundamental Theorem of Integral Calculus." Since all of the functions which will arise in this course relating to this topic will have antiderivatives, it would be inefficient to take up the definite integral. This would amount to preparing a way for introducing certain complications and then taking additional steps to avoid them. Fortunately there is a more direct route to the applications than that provided by the definite integral and the Fundamental Theorem, and the symbol $\int_a^b f(x)dx$ will be used merely as an abbreviation for $F(b)-F(a)$, where F is any antiderivative of f. However, the reader should be aware that, in addition to its present meaning as an abbreviation, and completely compatible with this meaning, the symbol $\int_a^a f(x)dx$ has a far more complex meaning in more sophisticated settings. (See Appendix C for details.)

Exercises

1. Find $f(x)$ if $f(3) = 0$ and if $f'(x)$ is

    (a) x^2 (d) $(x-3)^2$ (g) $\sqrt{1+x}$

    (b) x^2-x (e) $(2x+3)^3$ (h) $\sqrt{1+2x}$

    (c) $3x^2+2x+1$ (f) x^{500} (i) $\sqrt{a+bx}$

2. Express each of the parts of Exercise 1 in the form $\int_a^b g(x)$.

    (a) Prove that if $|f'(x)| \le M$ for every x in some interval I, then $|f(a)-f(b)| \le M|a-b|$ for every a and b of I.

    (b) What is the corresponding conclusion if $|f'(x)| \ge M$ for every x in I? It is true?

3. The function f is *strictly increasing* in an interval (a, b) if, for every p, q of the interval, $p < q$ implies $f(p) < f(q)$. Show that if $f(x) > 0$ for every x in (a, b), then f is strictly increasing in (a, b). What are the corresponding facts for strictly decreasing functions? What modifications are called for if the requirement "strictly" is omitted and the discussion is broadened to include all increasing and decreasing functions? Show that if f is strictly increasing and continuous in (a, b), then its inverse exists, is strictly increasing, and is continuous on (a, b).

4. (Parametric Equations)   If f and g are functions, then each number t in their domain determines the point $(f(t), g(t))$. If f and g are continuous, the set of all these points is a *curve* and the equations $x = f(t)$, $y = g(t)$ are *parametric* equations for this curve.

   (a)   Show that if f has an inverse, then this curve is the graph of $g \circ f^{-1}$.

   (b)   Show that if f has an inverse and if f and g are differentiable, the slope of the tangent to this curve at $(f(t), g(t))$ is $g'(t)/f'(t)$.

   (c)   Show that the curve defined by $x = 1/(1+t^2)$, $y = t/(1+t^2)$ is a circle.

   (d)   Find the slope of its tangent both by using part (a) and also by using part (b), and compare your answers.

Applications of the Antiderivative

In this section a single method is used to derive formulas for a variety of geometric items. In each case Theorem 4-6 is used to identify the derivative of the unknown function and then Corollary 4-12 is used to find the function itself. A noteworthy feature of the method is that it furnishes extremely definite answers to somewhat vague questions—it gives formulas for items which are not even completely defined, but only described by general stipulations. The method can be used successfully in many other areas besides geometry. Some of the exercises which accompany this section indicate a few of these applications.

I. *Area under a curve:* Let f be a continuous function whose values are positive. Then the points of a vertical strip which are below the graph of f and above the x-axis form a figure whose area can be expressed in terms of derivatives. Let us seek a formula $F(x)$ for the area of the figure (see figure) bounded by the graph of f, the x-axis, the vertical line through A, and the vertical line through X, where X is the

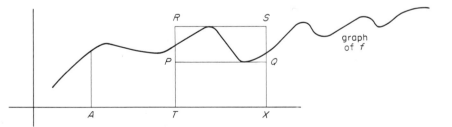

point on the x-axis whose abscissa is x. Even though we do not have a precise definition of area we can surely assert the following:

(1) If T is between X and A and if t is its abscissa, then $F(x)-F(t)$ is the area of the figure bounded by the graph of f, the x-axis, the line PT, and the line QX.

(2) The area of the figure described in (1) is not less than the area of the rectangle $PQXT$, since this rectangle lies wholly in the figure.

(3) The area of the figure described in (1) is not greater than that of the rectangle $RSXT$, since it lies wholly in that rectangle.

It follows from these assertions that if $x > t$, then

$$(x-t)\underline{f} \leq F(x)-F(t) \leq (x-t)\bar{f}.$$

It follows from Corollary 4-7 that $F'(x) = f(x)$. This does not by any means tell us what $F(x)$ is, but it helps. In fact, if we can find a function G such that $G' = f$, then, because $F(a) = 0$, Corollary 4-12 tells us that $F(x) = G(x)-G(a)$.

Example: To find the area $F(x)$ under the graph of $y = x^2$ from a to x we recall that $F'(x) = x^2$. We know that $x^3/3$ has x^2 for its derivative and we know that $F(a) = 0$. Corollary 4-12 tells us that

$$F(x) = \frac{x^3}{3} - \frac{a^3}{3}.$$

II. *Area "under" a curve* (continued): There is nothing in the conditions $F'(x) = f(x)$, $F(a) = 0$ which requires f to have only positive values. It is tempting to see if the function F which obeys these conditions also has an area interpretation if f has negative values. It is not difficult to see that the following holds about such as F:

(1) it assigns positive area to figures above the x-axis;

(2) it assigns negative areas to figures below the x-axis, and to figures which lie partly above and partly below, it assigns the algebraic sum of these portions.

Example: The graph of $y = x-x^2$ is shown in the figure below. Since $(x^2/2-(x^3/3)$ has derivative $x-x^2$, we see that

$$F(x) = (x^2/2)-(x^3/3)-5/6$$

is the unique $F(x)$ for which $F'(x) = x - x^2$ and $F(-1) = 0$. Consequently, $F(x)$ is a formula for the area "under" the graph of $y = x - x^2$

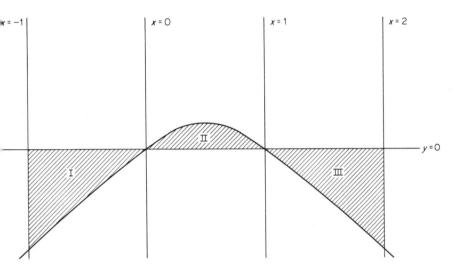

between -1 and x. Its value at 2, namely, $-3/2$, is the sum $-5/6 + 1/6 + 5/6$ of areas I, II, III taken with the proper signs. It is instructive to verify this.

III. *Volumes of figures with known cross sections:* Suppose a solid V is bounded by the planes $s = a$ and $x = b$, and, for every t between a and b the cross section V cut out by the plane $x = t$ has area $f(t)$. Then the volume of the figure can be found as follows: let $F(t)$ be the volume of the portion of V bounded by the planes $x = a$ and $x = t$, for $a \leq t \leq b$, and make the "plausible assumptions":

(1) The volume of the portion of V between $x = x_2$ and $x = x_1$ is $F(x_2) - F(x_1)$;

(2) $(x_2 - x_1)\underline{f} \leq F(x_2) - F(x_1) \leq (x_2 - x_1)\overline{f}$ where $\underline{f}$ is the minimum area of a cross section of V sliced out by a plane $x = w$, for w between x_1 and x_2 and where $\overline{f}$ is the maximum area so obtained.

The maximum and minimum values referred to in (2) will surely exist if f is continuous. If this additional stipulation is made, then we can conclude that $F' = f$, and $F(b) = \int_a^b f(x)dx$.

Example: Let V be the set of points inside the sphere $x^2+y^2+z^2 = r^2$, and let us use $x = -r$ and $x = r$ as the bounding planes. The cross section at $x = t$ is a circle of radius $(r^2-t^2)^{1/2}$ and which therefore has

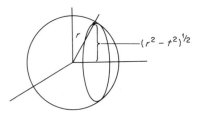

area $\pi(r^2-t^2)$. The volume function F has the properties $F(-r) = 0$, $F'(x) = \pi(r^2-x^2)$. Since $\pi r^2 x - (\pi x^2/3)$ is an antiderivative of $\pi(r^2-x^2)$, we infer that

$$F(x) = \pi r^2 x - \frac{\pi x^3}{3} - \left(-\pi r^3 + \frac{\pi r^3}{3}\right) = \pi r^2 x - \frac{\pi x^3}{3} + \frac{2}{3}\pi r^3$$

It follows that $F(r) = (4/3)\pi r^3$.

IV.   *Length of Arc:* We consider certain curves and seek a formula for the length of their arcs. We proceed without precise definitions of the terms in question, being guided only by plausible assumptions.

We consider a straight line to be a curve and consider its segments to be its arcs. More generally, we shall regard the graph of a continuous function as a curve, and the set of points on such a graph whose x-coordinates lie in some interval $[a, b]$ as the arc of this curve from a to b. We confine our study to this type of curve and derive a formula for its arc length if the function in question is not only continuous but differentiable.

For the line whose equation is $y = p+qx$, the arc length from a to b is the length of the segment whose end points are $(a, p+qa)$ and $(b, p+qb)$. Since the length of a segment is the distance between its end points, we see that the length is $\sqrt{(b-a)^2+(p+qb-p-qa)^2}$, which reduces to $(b-a)\sqrt{1+q^2}$. It follows that if we have a second segment with end points $(a, p'+q'a)$ and $(b, p'+q'b)$, then the length of the first will be greater than the length of the second if and only if $q^2 > q'^2$. This observation about segments is used as the basis for the following "plausible assumption" about more general arcs.

ASSUMPTION (1)   Let f be differentiable, and let M be a number such that $|f'(x)| \leq M$ for every x in $[a, b]$. Then the arc length of the graph of f from a to b is not greater than $(b-a)\sqrt{1+M^2}$. Similarly, if there is a number m such that $|f'(x)| \geq m$ for every x in $[a, b]$, then the arc length of the graph of f from a to b is not less than $(b-a)\sqrt{1+m^2}$.

We also need an assumption about the additivity of arc length.

ASSUMPTION (2)   If $a < b < c$, then the arc length from a to b plus the arc length from b to c is the arc length from a to c.

It follows from Assumption (2) that if $s(x)$ is a formula for the arc length from a to x and if $a < x < y$, then $s(y) - s(x)$ is a formula for the length of arc from x to y.

Combining these two plausible assumptions, we see that if $s(x)$ is the length of the arc of the graph of f from a to x, then $s(y) - s(x)$ is between $(y-x)\sqrt{1+m^2}$ and $(y-x)\sqrt{1+M^2}$, where m and M are, respectively, the minimum and maximum values of the derivative f' in $[x, y]$. Corollary 4-7 is now invoked to infer that $s'(x) = \sqrt{1+f'(x)^2}$. We conclude that the arc length from a to b is

$$\int_a^b \sqrt{1+f'(x)^2}\, dx.$$

Example: We find the arc length of the graph of f from a to b, if $f(x) = x^{3/2}$. Since $f'(x) = \tfrac{3}{2}x^{1/2}$, the length must be

$$\int_a^b \sqrt{1+(\tfrac{9}{4})x}\, dx.$$

Since $\tfrac{8}{27}(1+(\tfrac{9}{4})x)^{3/2}$ is an antiderivative of $\sqrt{1+(\tfrac{9}{4})x}$, we infer that the arc length from a to b is

$$\tfrac{8}{27}((1+(\tfrac{9}{4})b)^{3/2}-(1+(\tfrac{9}{4})a)^{3/2}).$$

V.   GRAVITATIONAL ATTRACTION: We occasionally need a more elaborate version of Corollary 4-7, which is a variant of a result called "Duhamel's Principle." It states:

Let f and g be continuous throughout the interval (a, b), and suppose for every x and t of this interval that $F(x) - F(t)$ is between $fg(x - t)$

and $f\bar{g}(x-t)$, where, $\underline{f}\underline{g}$ and f, g, are the minimum and maximum values, respectively, of f and g in the closed interval $[x, t]$. Then F is differentiable, and $F'(x) = f(x)g(x)$ for every x in (a, b).

This theorem is readily proved by showing that $F(x) - F(t) - f(t)g(t)(x-t)$ has order one at t. The details are left to the reader.

We show how this theorem enables us to compute the gravitational attraction of a rod of variable density on a particle located on the line of the rod. Suppose that the rod is located on the x-axis, extending from a to b, that its density at each x is $d(x)$, and that the particle has mass m and position coordinate c. Suppose also that c is outside $[a, b]$. We denote by $F(x)$ the gravitational attraction exerted by the portion of the rod which lies between a and x, and make the following "plausible assumptions."

(1) The attraction exerted by the portion of the rod which lies between x and t is $F(x) - F(t)$.

(2) The attraction of the portion of the rod which lies between x and t is overestimated if we overestimate its mass by assuming that its density is constant and equal to $\bar{d}$, and then imagine all this mass concentrated at that point of $[x, t]$ which is nearest to c.

(3) The attraction of the portion of the rod which lies between x and t is underestimated if we underestimate its mass by assuming that its density is constant and equal to $\underline{d}$, and then imagine this mass concentrated at the point of $[x, t]$ farthest from c.

Recall the formula $m_1 m_2/d_{12}{}^2$ for the gravitational force between particles of masses m_1 and m_2 and mutual distance d_{12}. With reference to this formula our assumptions state that $F(x) - F(t)$ is between $f\bar{d}(x-t)$ and $\underline{f}\underline{d}(x-t)$, where $f(w)$ is $1/(c-w)^2$. Duhamel's principle then implies that $F'(x) = md(x)/(c-w)^2$. We conclude that the total force is

$$\int_a^b \frac{md(x)}{(c-x)^2}$$

Exercises

1. Find the area under the graph of   (a) x^2 from -1 to 3;   (b) $x^{1/2}$ from 1 to 4;   (c) x^{-2} from 1 to t. Show that this area is less than 1, no matter how large t is.

2. Determine t so that the area under the graph of $x-x^2$ from -1 to t is
    (a) positive; (b) 0; (c) negative.

3. Find the volume of the solid whose base is a circle of radius R and each
    of whose cross sections perpendicular to a fixed diameter of the base
    is a (a) square; (b) equilateral triangle; (c) isosceles right tri-
    angle; (d) semicircle.

4   (Solid of revolution) Prove that if the graph of f is revolved around
    the x-axis the volume of the resulting solid of revolution cut off by the
    planes $x = a$ and $x = b$ is $\int_a^b \pi f^2$. Apply this result to derive formulas
    for the volume of a cylinder, a cone, and a sphere.

5. Express as a definite integral the arc length of each of the curves of
    Exercise 1 (do not try to evaluate these integrals).

6. Derive a formula for the arc length of the curve whose parametric
    equations are $x = f(t), y = g(t)$.

7. Let the points $P_1, P_2, \ldots, P_n$ have coordinates (x_1, y_1), (x_2, y_2), $\ldots$,
    (x_n, y_n), where $x_1 < x_2 < \cdots < x_n$, and let C be the polygonal path
    consisting of the segments $P_1P_2, P_2P_3, \ldots, P_{n-1}P_n$. (a) What is the
    length of C?   (b) State and prove for C the appropriate versions of
    the plausible assumptions of this section about arc length.

Applications of the Derivative

Many of the important functions which arise in applications of
mathematics have derivatives. It is a fairly safe principle to assert that
if a differentiable function expresses some important relation, then so
does its derivative. Sometimes a problem is solved simply by recognizing
that the function which is sought is the derivative of a known function,
and often this recognition is prompted by an awareness of a special
interpretation of derivatives. We consider some interpretations now.

I. SPEEDS AS DERIVATIVES: Consider a particle moving along a
line. If we choose a coordinate system for the line and a coordinate
system for time (a reference clock), there is a function F whose value
$F(x)$ is the position coordinate of the particle at time x. We assert that
if this function F is differentiable, its derivative at time x is a formula
for the speed of the moving particle at time x. There are several ways
to see this. One common one is to *define* speed in this way and then to

give evidence that this is a good definition. We prefer to leave the definition of speed to the physicists, and to show how to deduce this conclusion about speed, without an explicit definition, merely by using a few plausible assumptions. We suppose of this moving particle that at each time x it has a speed $f(x)$. We assume that if a time difference $x-t$ is multiplied by the maximum speed $\bar{f}$ which occurs in the time interval $[t, x]$, the product $(x-t)\bar{f}$ is not less than the actual distance $F(x)-F(t)$ travelled in that interval. We assume, similarly, that $(x-t)\underline{f}$ is not greater than $F(x)-F(t)$, where $\underline{f}$ is the minimum speed which occurs in $[t, x]$. If we further agree that f is continuous, it follows from Corollary 4-7 that $F'(x) = f(x)$.

Examples:

(a)   It has been shown experimentally that a body in a vacuum released from rest at time 0 falls $16x^2$ feet in x seconds. We infer that the derivative of $16x^2$, namely, $32x$, is its speed at time x (in feet per second). This has been confirmed experimentally.

(b)   If a body is thrown with initial speed v_0 feet per second from initial height h_0 feet, its height at x seconds is given by $h_0+v_0x-16x^2$. Thus its speed at time x is given by v_0-32x feet per second. If v_0 is positive, then at $v_0/32$ seconds the speed is 0. This corresponds to the time at which the body stops rising and begins to fall. If v_0 is negative, then $v_0/32$ is also negative and corresponds to a time outside the range being considered. In this case the body was thrown downward and does not rise at all.

The derivative of the speed function is a formula for acceleration. This can be either taken as a definition or deduced by an argument like the one which identified the speed formula as the derivative of the distance function. In Examples (a) and (b) above, the acceleration is seen to be constant. This expresses the facts that a body falling only under the influence of gravity, near the surface of the earth, has a constant force acting on it, and therefore (according to a law of physics), has a constant acceleration. The constant acceleration is positive in the first example and negative in the second because the coordinate systems in the two examples were oppositely oriented.

Note: In working with functions we deal with numbers, not with distances or times. In discussing the motion of a body by means of functions, we must interpret the numbers in terms of appropriate units in order for them to be significant. For instance, if x_1 and x_2 are the coordinates of the points on a line, then the distance between these points is $|x_2-x_1|$ relative to the unit distance given by the point pair consisting of the origin and the point with coordinate one. If x_1 and x_2 are the time coordinates of two instants, then the length of the time interval they determine is $|x_1-x_2|$ relative to the unit on which the time coordinate system is based.

II. CHANGE AND RATE OF CHANGE: Consider the function F defined by $F(x) = \pi x^2$. For every positive number r, we see that $F(r)$ is the area of all circles of radius r. Thus $F(b)-F(a)$ is the change in area of a circle whose radius changes from a to b. This language of change is frequently applied to the functions themselves, rather than to the processes they describe. We shall say that if a and b are any numbers in the domain of a function F, then the difference $F(b)-F(a)$ is the *change in F* corresponding to $b-a$, the *change in x*.

It is customary to speak of the rate at which changes take place. Plausible assumptions about this otherwise undefined concept enable us to find a formula for the rate of change of F in certain cases, and the formula in question is precisely F', as will be shown. In fact, the phrase "rate of change" is sometimes used as a synonym for "derivative" in calculus textbooks.

Given the function F, we seek a function f whose value at x is the rate of change of F at x. We assume that if $[x, y]$ is any interval in the domain of F and if $\bar{f}$ and f are the maximum and minimum values of f in this interval, then the change $F(y)-F(x)$ is between $(y-x)f$ and $(y-x)\bar{f}$. It follows from Corollary 4-7 that $f = F'$.

The rate of change of a function is the derivative of that function and involves no ambiguity. This is not the case for the rate of change of quantities described by functions, since a given quantity can generally be described by many different functions, depending on different variables and different rates of change. For instance, the volume of a sphere, in terms of its radius r, is $\frac{4}{3}\pi r^3$, whereas this volume in terms of the diameter d is $\frac{1}{6}\pi d^3$, and in terms of the surface area A the volume is $(\frac{1}{6}\sqrt{\pi})A^{3/2}$. Each of these three different functions has a derivative and each of these three different derivatives is an acceptable formula for the rate of change of volume. This ambiguity is generally avoided by indicating the variable being considered. Thus "the rate of change of the volume of a sphere with respect to its radius" specifies the function f for which $f(r) = \frac{4}{3}\pi r^3$ and whose rate of change f' is specified by $f'(r) = 4\pi r^2$; "the rate of change of the volume of a sphere with respect to its area" specifies the function g for which $g(A) = (1/6\sqrt{\pi})A^{3/2}$ and whose rate of change g' is specified by $g'(A) = (1/4\sqrt{\pi})A^{1/2}$.

Examples:

(a)   The formula $A(r) = \pi r^2$ expresses the area of a circle in terms of its radius. Therefore $A'(r) = 2\pi r$ is a formula for the rate of change of the area with respect to the radius. Suppose that the radius changes with time and that $R(t)$ is a formula for the radius at time t. Then $R'(t)$ is the rate of change of the radius with respect to time, at time t. In this case the area also is a function $A \circ R$ of time, and its derivative $(A \circ R)'$, evaluated at t, gives the rate of change of area with respect to time. If, for instance, $R(t) = 3t$, then

$$(A \circ R)'(t) = A'(R(t))R'(t) = 2\pi(3t)3 = 18\pi t.$$

(b)   Since l^3 is the formula for the volume of the cube whose edges have length l, it follows that $3l^2$ is a formula for the rate of change of this volume with respect to this edge. The formula which expresses the length of the edge in terms of the volume is the inverse of that which expresses the volume in terms of the length of the edge. Theorem 4-13 enables us to conclude that $1/(3l^2)$ is a formula for the rate of change of the length of the edge of a cube with respect to its volume.

III.   DIFFERENTIAL EQUATIONS.   Sometimes the information about an unknown function involves derivatives in a way we have not yet considered. For instance, suppose that at time x_0 a certain quantity of radioactive substance is observed and a formula is sought for the amount remaining at time x. If the unknown formula is $F(x)$, then, on general mathematical principles, the rate of change of the amount is $F'(x)$. Principles of physics supply the information that the rate of change is proportional to the amount itself, that is, there is a number c such that $F'(x) = cF(x)$. The novelty here is that the unknown function's derivative is expressed in terms of the unknown function itself, so we cannot use our earlier methods of solution, which depended on expressing the unknown function as a derivative or an antiderivative of a known function. This new type of equation is an example of a differential equation. Although we cannot solve this problem now, we shall be able to do so readily when we have studied the exponential function. It is a noteworthy fact that this equation and the value $F(x_0)$ completely determine the unknown function F.

An apparently different problem comes from the study of colonies of bacteria. Here, under idealized conditions of growth, the rate of growth of the colony is proportional to the size of the colony. If $F(x)$ is a formula for the size of the colony at time x, then $F'(x)$ is a formula for its rate of change. There must be a number c such that $F'(x) = cF(x)$. Thus the same equations that described the size of a shrinking radioactive substance also describe the size of the growing colony of bacteria. In the first case $c < 0$, and $c > 0$ in the second.

Exercises

1. The position coordinate of a body at time t is $10 - 3t - 4t^2 + t^3$. (a) What is its speed at time t? (b) What is its acceleration at time t? (c) At what time does it attain its minimum speed? (d) At what time is its speed 0?

2. The height above the ground at time t of a body is given by the formula $100 + 18t - 16t^2$. What is its maximum height? What is its minimum speed? If it takes a seconds for the body to go from height h to its maximum height, what is h in terms of a? If it takes b seconds to fall from its maximum height to height h, what is h in terms of b?

3. If the radius of a circle is increasing at 2 feet per second, what is the rate of change of the area and of the circumference, with respect to the radius, when the radius is 0, 1, 2, R?

4. V and S are the volume and surface area of the sphere of radius R. Find the rate of change of each of V, S, R with respect to each of the others.

5. The position coordinates of a body at time t are $x = f(t)$, $y = g(t)$. Prove that its speed at time t is $\sqrt{f'(t)^2 + g'(t)^2}$. [Hint: Consider the speed as the rate of change of arc length with respect to time.]

Higher Derivatives, Taylor's Theorem

The derivative of a function is itself a function and may have its own derivative. In this section we study functions whose derivatives are also differentiable.

DEFINITION: If f is differentiable and if its derivative f' is also differentiable, we call the derivative $(f')'$ the *second* derivative of f. Higher derivatives are defined by the rule that the $(n-1)$-st derivative of f' is the n-th derivative of f, for $n = 3, 4, \ldots$.

Notation: $f', f'', f''', f^{IV}, \ldots, f^{(n)}, f^{(n+1)}, \ldots$ denote, respectively, the (first) derivative of f, the second, third, fourth, $\ldots$, n-th, $(n+1)$-st, $\ldots$. Sometimes it is convenient to consider $f^{(0)}$ to mean f.

Since polynomial functions are differentiable and since their derivatives are also polynomial functions, we see that polynomial functions have derivatives of every order. There are functions other than polynomial functions that have this property. There are also functions which do not have derivatives of any order, and for every positive integer n there are functions which have derivatives of all orders up to n but not of order $n+1$. It is clear that if f has an n-th derivative, it must have derivatives of all orders less than n. The next theorem is a generalization of the Mean Value Theorem. The Mean Value Theorem expresses the value of a function at b in terms of its value at a and its derivative at an intermediate point. The following theorem provides an analagous expression for the value of a function at b using higher derivatives.

THEOREM 4-14 (Taylor's Theorem): Let n be a nonnegative integer, let I be an interval, and let f be a function which has a derivative of order $n+1$ at each point of I. Then if a and b are any distinct points of I, there is a c strictly between them such that

$$f(b) = f(a) + f'(a)(b-a) + \cdots + \frac{f^{(i)}(a)(b-a)^i}{i!} + \cdots$$

$$+ \frac{f^{(n)}(a)(b-a)^n}{n!} + \frac{f^{(n+1)}(c)(b-a)^{n+1}}{(n+1)!}.$$

Proof: Define the auxiliary function F by

$$F(x) = f(x) - f(a) - f'(a)(x-a) - \cdots$$

$$- \frac{f^{(n)}(a)(x-a)^n}{n!} - \frac{k}{(n+1)!}(x-a)^{n+1},$$

where k is the number which makes $F(b) = 0$. Then, since $F(a) = 0$ as well, Rolle's Theorem implies that there is a c_1, strictly between a and b, such that $F'(c_1) = 0$. A simple calculation shows that $F'(a) = 0$ as well. Rolle's Theorem implies that there is a c_2, strictly between a and c_1, such that $f''(c_2) = 0$. Continuing to argue in this way, we see that for each i less than or equal to n we have $F^{(i)}(a) = F^{(i)}(c_1) = 0$, where c_i is strictly between a and c_{i-1}. In particular, we have $F^{(n)}(a) = F^{(n)}(c_n) = 0$. Thus there is a c_{n+1}, strictly between a and c_n, such that $F^{(n+1)}(c_{n+1}) = 0$. But $F^{(n+1)}(x) = f^{(n+1)}(x) - k$. It follows that $k = f^{(n+1)}(c_{n+1})$.

COROLLARY 4-15: If $f^{(n+1)}(x) = 0$ for every x in I, then f is defined by a polynomial of degree at most n.

COROLLARY 4-16: If $f^{(n+1)}$ is continuous in I, then f is of class $P(t, n+1)$ at each t in I and its $(t, n+1)$ approximation is

$$f(t) + f'(t)(x-t) + \cdots + \frac{f^{(i)}(t)(x-t)^i}{i!} + \cdots + \frac{f^{(n+1)}(t)(x-t)^{n+1}}{(n+1)!}.$$

Proof: The difference between $f(x)$ and its proposed $(t, n+1)$ approximation is

$$\frac{f^{(n+1)}(c) - f^{(n+1)}(t)}{(n+1)!}(x-t)^{n+1}.$$

Since $f^{(n+1)}$ is continuous, this expression is of order $n+1$ at t.

COROLLARY 4-17: If $f^{(n+1)}$ is bounded in I, then f is of class $P(t, n)$ at each t of I, and its (t, n) approximation is

$$f(t) + f'(t)(x-t) + \cdots + \frac{f^{(n)}(t)(x-t)^n}{n!}.$$

Proof: The difference between $f(x)$ and its proposed (t, n) approximation is

$$\frac{f^{(n+1)}(c)(x-t)^{n+1}}{(n+1)!}.$$

Since $f^{(n+1)}(c)/(n+1)!$ is bounded, this is of order n at t.

COROLLARY 4-18: Let M be an upper bound for $|f^{(n+1)}|$ in I. Then

$$|f(x) - P(x)| \leq \frac{M}{(n+1)!}|x-t|^{n+1}$$

where x and t are any points of I and where $P(x)$ is the (t, n) approximation to f.

This corollary sometimes helps us to appraise the accuracy of (t, n) approximations. We have known that the values of these approximations at x are close to the corresponding function values at x provided that x is sufficiently close to t. However, there has been no indication of how close x must actually be to t to achieve a given standard of accuracy. Corollary 4-18 provides such an indication.

Example: Let $f(x) = (1-x)^{-1}$. Then $f'(x) = -1(1-x)^{-2}$, $f''(x) = 1-2(1-x)^{-3}, \ldots, f^{(n)}(x) = n!(1-x)^{-(n+1)}$. If I is $-\frac{1}{2} \leq x \leq \frac{1}{2}$, then $(n+1)! 2^{n+2}$ is an upper bound for $f^{(n+1)}$ on I. It follows that $|f(x) - P(x)| \leq 2^{n+2} |x-t|^{n+1}$. For instance, if $n = 5$, $t = 0$, $x = \frac{1}{20}$, we have $|f(x) - P(x)| \leq 0.00002$.

Note: The $(0, 5)$ approximation to the f of the previous example is $1 + x + x^2 + x^3 + x^4 + x^5$ and $f(x) - P(x) = x^6/(1-x)$. At $x = \frac{1}{20}$ this has the value $\frac{20}{19}(\frac{1}{20})^6$, which is considerably smaller than the estimate obtained by using Corollary 4-18. To understand why Corollary 4-18 is important even though it can grossly overestimate errors, we must understand how Corollary 4-18 is actually used. In practice it is often necessary to estimate with some specified accuracy an $f(x)$ whose exact value is not known. Corollary 4-18 can often supply a guarantee that for a certain t and n the (t, n) approximation to f meets the given standard of accuracy.

Exercises

1. If $f(x) = \sqrt{1+x}$,
    (a) compute $f'(x), f''(x), f'''(x), f^{(IV)}(x)$.
    (b) Use Taylor's Theorem with $a = 0$, $b = 0.1$, $n = 3$ to compute $\sqrt{1.1}$ and estimate the error.

2. (a) Find $\sqrt[3]{9}$ correct to three decimal places. [Hint: Use Taylor's Theorem with $f(x) = \sqrt[3]{x}$, $a = 8$, $b = 9$].
    (b) Find $1/11^4$ with an error less than 0.000001.
    (c) Find $\sqrt[3]{65}$ with an error less than 0.001.

3. Let f and g be functions and let h be $g \circ f^{-1}$. Find a formula for h'' in terms of f, g, f', g', f'', g''. Find h'' if
    (a) $f(t) = t^2 + 1$, $g(t) = t + 1$;
    (b) $f(t) = t + 1$, $g(t) = t^2$;
    (c) $f(t) = 1/(t^2 + 1)$, $g(t) = t/(t^2 + 1)$.

4. (L'Hopital's Rule extended) Show that if f and g have derivatives up to order n at t, if

$$0 = f(t) = f'(t) = \cdots = f^{(n-1)}(t) = g(t) = g'(t) = \cdots = g^{(n-1)}(t)$$

and if $g^{(n)}(t) \neq 0$, then

$$\lim_{x \to t} \frac{f(x)}{g(x)} = \frac{f^{(n)}(t)}{g^{(n)}(t)}.$$

5. The graph of f is *concave upward* in an interval if and only if, for every p, q, r of that interval with $p < q < r$, the slope of the line connecting $(p, f(p))$ and $(q, f(q))$ is less than the slope of the line connecting $(q, f(q))$ and $(r, f(r))$.

   (a) Show that if f is differentiable in an interval, and if f' is increasing in that interval, then the graph of f is concave upward in that interval.

   (b) Show that if f'' is positive in some interval, then the graph of f is concave upward in that interval.

   (c) State the fact corresponding to parts (a) and (b) of this problem for regions in which a graph is concave upward.

   (d) Show that the graph of a quadratic polynomial is either concave upward or concave downward throughout its entire extent.

   (e) Classify the graphs of cubic polynomials according to the regions in which they are concave upward.

6. Show that if $f'(t) = 0$, $f''(t) \neq 0$, then f has either a relative maximum or a relative minimum at t, depending on the sign of $f''(t)$. Discuss the behavior of f at t if $f'(t) = f''(t) = \cdots = f^{(n-1)}(t) = 0$, $f^{(n)}(t) \neq 0$ in relation to the value of n and the sign of $f^{(n)}(t)$.

CHAPTER 5

Infinite Sequences and Infinite Series

One of the most important features of "modern" (after 1650) mathematics is its treatment of infinite sets and processes. We are going to study a topic now in which infinite processes are central, and the student who masters it will have made a good start toward understanding the kind of mathematics which has been developed during the last three centuries.

Most students have already had some exposure to the subject of convergence of infinite sequences and series. Anyone who has reflected on the connection between $\frac{1}{3}$ and $0.333\ldots$, or between $\sqrt{2}$ and $1.414\ldots$ or between π and $3.14159\ldots$ has encountered this topic. It is helpful, at the outset, to realize that common sense alone is not enough to develop the subject. Many famous and intelligent philosophers found only paradox and confusion when studying the infinite. We must be prepared to meet delicate and elaborate methods of studying these topics, which are not off-the-cuff, common-sense methods, but which seem to be (and are) rather sophisticated. Our reward will be to learn useful ways of constructing new numbers and functions and to solve important problems by using these constructions.

Convergence of Infinite Sequences

The connection between the sequence $0.3, 0.33, 0.333, \ldots$ and $\frac{1}{3}$ can be described informally by saying that every term far out in the sequence is near $\frac{1}{3}$. The following definitions formalize this situation involving a sequence, a number, and a relation between them, based on the concept of "far out" and "nearness."

DEFINITIONS: Let $a_0, a_1, a_2, \ldots$ be a sequence of numbers and let s be a number. We say that s is the *limit* of the sequence if and only if, for each positive number e, there is a positive integer N such that if $n > N$ then $|a_n - s| < e$. A sequence which has a limit s is said to be *convergent* and is said to *converge to s*. A sequence which has no limit is said to *diverge* or to be *divergent*.

Notation: We indicate that s is the limit of $a_0, a_1, a_2, \ldots$ by the symbols $\lim_{n \to \infty} a_n = s$ (read "the limit of a_n as n becomes infinite is s") and by the symbols $a_n \to s$ (read "a_n converges to s").

Examples:

(a) The sequence $1, 1/2, 1/3, \ldots, 1/n, \ldots$ converges to 0. To see this observe that $|0 - 1/n| = 1/n$. For every positive number e there is an integer N such that $N > 1/e$ (principle of Archimedes). Therefore $1/N < e$, and if $n > N$ we have $1/n < 1/N < e$.

(b) The sequence $1, 1, 1, \ldots, 1, \ldots$ has limit 1.

(c) The sequence $0, 1, 0, 1, \ldots$ is divergent.

(d) The sequence $0, 1, 2, 3, \ldots$ is divergent.

DEFINITION: A *subsequence* of the sequence $a_0, a_1, a_2, \ldots$ is any sequence $a_{i_0}, a_{i_1}, a_{i_2}, \ldots$ whose terms are terms of given sequence and whose subscripts satisfy $i_0 < i_1 < i_2 < \cdots$.

Note: It follows immediately from the definition of convergence that if $a_0, a_1, a_2, \ldots$ is a sequence which converges to s, then every subsequence of this sequence also converges to s.

Example: The sequence $1, 1/2, 1/2^2, 1/2^3, \ldots$ is a subsequence of $1, \frac{1}{2}, \frac{1}{3}, \ldots$, and they both converge to 0.

On the other hand, it does not follow that if a subsequence of a sequence converges then the original sequence converges. For instance, $1, 1, 1, \ldots$ is a convergent subsequence of the divergent sequence $1, 0, 1, 0, \ldots$. However, for certain very special subsequences this conclusion is valid. It is easy to see, for instance, that if a subsequence is formed by dropping a *finite* number of terms from an infinite sequence and then "closing ranks," the original sequence converges if and only if the subsequence converges.

It is not always necessary to invoke the definition of convergence to decide whether or not any given sequence converges. There are theorems which certify whole classes of sequences as convergent. The following definitions enable us to formulate one such theorem.

DEFINITIONS: The sequence $a_0, a_1, \ldots, a_n, \ldots$ is *monotonically increasing* if $a_0 \leq a_1 \leq a_2, \ldots$ and is *monotonically decreasing* if

$$a_0 \geq a_1 \geq a_2 \geq \ldots.$$

A sequence is *bounded* if there is a number M such that

$$|a_n| \leq M \text{ for } n = 0, 1, 2, \ldots.$$

THEOREM 5-1: A monotonically increasing bounded sequence converges to the least upper bound of its set of terms. A monotonically decreasing bounded sequence converges to the greatest lower bound of its set of terms.

Proof: Let $a_0, a_1, a_2, \ldots$ be a bounded monotonically increasing sequence and let M be the least upper bound of its set of terms. If e is any positive number, $M-e$, being less than M, is not an upper bound for the a_i. There is, therefore, some a_N such that $a_N > M-e$. Because the sequence is monotonic, if $n > N$ we also have $a_n > M-e$. But we also know that $a_n < M+e$ for every a because M is an upper bound for the a_i. It follows that $|M-a_n| < e$ and that $a_n \to M$.

The proof for monotonically decreasing sequences is similar.

COROLLARY 5-2: $1/2, 2/3, \ldots, n/n+1, \ldots$ has limit 1.

COROLLARY 5-3: If a and r are numbers for which $|r| < 1$, then $|ar^n| \to 0$ and $ar^n \to 0$.

Exercises

1. (a) Find an N such that $|\frac{1}{3} - a_n| < (0.1)^{10}$ for $n > N$.
   (b) Prove that 0.3, 0.33, 0.333, ... converges to $\frac{1}{3}$.

2. Prove that if $a_n \to s$ and $a_n \to t$, then $t = s$.

3. Prove that if $a_n \to s$ and $a_i < M$ for $i = 0, 1, 2, \ldots$, then $s \leq M$.

4. Prove that if $a_n \to s$, then $ca_n \to cs$.

5. Prove that if $a_n \to s$ and $b_n \to t$, then $a_n + b_n \to s + t$ and $a_n b_n \to st$.

6. Prove that if $a_n \to s$ and if $s \neq 0$, then there is an N such that $a_n \neq 0$ if $n > N$.

7. Prove that if r is any number, then $r^n/n! \to 0$.

8. Prove that if the sequence $a_0, a_1, a_2, \ldots$ is bounded and if $|r| < 1$, then $a_n r^n \to 0$.

9. Prove that if a sequence converges it is bounded.

10. Let S be a nonempty set of numbers which is bounded but which has no largest element. Prove that there is a monotonically increasing sequence whose terms belong to S and which converges to the least upper bound of S.

11. Prove that

$$\frac{1}{2}, \frac{1}{3} + \frac{1}{4}, \frac{1}{4} + \frac{1}{5} + \frac{1}{6} + \frac{1}{7} + \frac{1}{8}, \ldots, \frac{1}{n+1} + \frac{1}{n+2} + \cdots + \frac{1}{2n}, \ldots$$

is unbounded and monotonically increasing.

12. Prove that

$$1, 1 + \frac{1}{2}, 1 + \frac{1}{2} + \frac{1}{3}, \ldots, 1 + \frac{1}{2} + \frac{1}{3} + \cdots + \frac{1}{n}, \ldots$$

is unbounded. [Hint: Use the grouping of Exercise 11.]

13. Suppose that $a_0, a_1, a_2, \ldots$ and s are in the domain of the continuous function f. Prove that if $a_n \to s$, then $f(a_n) \to f(s)$.

14. Prove that if $a_n \to s$, then $\dfrac{a_1 + a_2 + \cdots + a_n}{n} \to s$. [Hint: Choose M so large that $|s - a_n| < e/2$ if $n > M$. Write $s - \dfrac{a_1 + \cdots + a_n}{n}$ as

$$\frac{(s - a_n) + \cdots + (s - a_{M+1})}{n} + \frac{(s - a_1) + \cdots + (s - a_M)}{n}$$

and notice that the term on the left is less than $e/2$ and the term on the right has a fixed numerator and large denominator.]

Cauchy Sequences

Since the terms far out in a convergent sequence must be close to their limit they must also be close to one another. Our next theorem and proof formalize this remark.

THEOREM 5-4: If $a_n \to s$ and if e is a positive number, then there is an integer N such that $|a_n - a_m| < e$ if $n > N$ and $m > N$.

Proof: There is an N such that $|s - a_n| < e/2$ if $n > N$. If $m > N$, we have

$$|a_n - a_m| = |a_n - s + s - a_m| \le |a_n - s| + |s - a_m| < e/2 + e/2 = e.$$

The converse of this theorem is also valid but is much harder to prove. This theorem and its converse state, very roughly, that a sequence converges if and only if, after a certain point, no significant changes occur in its terms. Of course the "certain point" depends on what we mean by "significant change." The theorems state that a sequence converges if and only if, no matter how small the change we might regard as significant, there exists a place beyond which no change as great as this occurs.

Before this converse is proved, an important fact about bounded sequences will be established.

THEOREM 5-5 (Bolzano-Weierstrass Theorem): Every bounded infinite sequence has a convergent subsequence.

Proof: Let $a_0, a_1, a_2, \ldots$ be the sequence and let S be the set of numbers x such that for infinitely many subscripts i we have $x \le a_i$. Then S is not empty, because if B is a lower bound for $\{a_0, a_1, a_2, \ldots\}$, then B is in S. Moreover if B_2 is an upper bound for $\{a_0, a_1, a_2, \ldots\}$ then it is also an upper bound for S. It follows that S has a least upper bound b. If c is any number less than b, then there are infinitely many i for which a_i is between c and b. Let a_{i_0} be a term of the sequence between $b-1$ and b, let a_{i_1} be a term of the sequence between $b - \frac{1}{2}$ and b, with i_1 greater than i_0, and in general, let a_{i_n} be a term of the sequence between $b - 1/(n+1)$ and b with i_n greater than i_{n-1}, for $n = 0, 1, 2, \ldots$. Then the subsequence $a_{i_0}, a_{i_1}, a_{i_2}, \ldots$ converges to b.

DEFINITION: The sequence a_0, a_1, a_2, ... is a *Cauchy* sequence if, for every $e > 0$, there is a positive integer N such that $|a_n - a_m| < e$ if $n > N$, $m > N$.

Examples:

(a) Let I be the interval $[0, 1]$, let I_1 be one of the two intervals obtained by bisecting I, let I_2 be one of the two intervals obtained by bisecting I_1, etc. Let a_0 be any point of I, let a_1 be any point of I_1, let a_2 be any point of I_2, etc. Then a_0, a_1, a_2, ... is a Cauchy sequence.

(b) Any convergent sequence.

The promised converse to Theorem 5-4 can now be proved.

THEOREM 5-6: Every Cauchy sequence converges.

Proof: Let a_0, a_1, a_2, ... be a Cauchy sequence. We show first that it is bounded. Choose N such that $|a_m - a_n| < 1$ if $m > N$, $n > N$. Then, since $N + 1 > N$, $|a_m| < 1 + |a_{N+1}|$ if $m > N$. Then no $|a_i|$ is greater than the largest of $|a_0|$, $|a_1|$, ..., $|a_n|$, $1 + |a_{N+1}|$, and the sequence is bounded. It follows that our sequence has a convergent subsequence a_{i_0}, a_{i_1}, a_{i_2}, ... Let this subsequence converge to s. We show that the original sequence also converges to s. For $e > 0$ choose N_1 so that $|a_{i_r} - s| < e/2$ if $i_r > N_1$, and choose N_2 so that $|a_n - a_m| < e/2$ if $n > N_2$, $m > N_2$. For every n and i_r we have $|a_n - s| \leq |a_n - a_{i_r}| + |a_{i_r} - s|$. If we choose N to be the larger of N_1 and N_2 then, if $n > N$ and if $i_r > N$, each term of the right is less than $e/2$. It follows that if $n > N$ we have $|a_n - s| < e$, whence $a_n \rightarrow s$.

It has been shown that every convergent sequence is a Cauchy sequence and that every Cauchy sequence is a convergent sequence. This might lead us to inquire why these two classifications are introduced, since they lead to the same end result. The answer is that this is not the case in general; it depends on the type of terms which appear in the sequence and the type of limit which is available. If, instead of considering real numbers, we had considered rational numbers only, all terms rational and all limits rational, then we would have found that the class of convergent sequences is much smaller than the class of Cauchy sequences. For instance, the sequence 3, 3.1, 3.14, 3.141, ... (successive decimal approximations to the irrational number π) is a Cauchy sequence of rational numbers but does not converge to a rational number. We say that the real number system is *complete* because all its Cauchy sequences converge to real numbers and that the rational number system is not complete because not all of its Cauchy sequences converge to rational numbers. Indeed, one way of constructing the real number system from the rational number system is to enlarge the latter to include the limits of its Cauchy sequences.

This study of functions will present a similar case of incompleteness and involve us in a similar extension program. The sequences will have terms which come from polynomial functions, and their limits will be the values of new, nonpolynomial functions.

Exercises

1. Show that each of the following is a Cauchy sequence.
   (a) $0.3, 0.33, 0.333, \ldots$
   (b) $3, 3.1, 3.14 \ldots$ (successive approximation to π)
   (c) $1, 1+\frac{1}{3}, 1+\frac{1}{3}+(\frac{1}{3})^2, \ldots$
   (d) $a_0, a_0+a_1(\frac{1}{3}), a_0+a_1(\frac{1}{3})+a_2(\frac{1}{3})^2, \ldots$ (a_i is either 0, 1 or 2)

2. Show that each of the following is not a Cauchy sequence.
   (a) $3, 33, 333, \ldots$
   (b) $1, 1+r, 1+r+r^2, \ldots$, where $|r| \geq 1$

3. Show that a bounded sequence which is not convergent has at least two convergent subsequences whose limits are different from one another.

4. (Nested Interval Principle)   Prove that if $I_0, I_1, I_2, \ldots$ are closed intervals such that each is a subset of its predecessor, then there is at least one point which is in all the intervals. [Hint: Pick a point in each interval, pick a convergent subsequence of these points, and show that the limit of this convergent sequence is in all the intervals.]

5. Let I_n be the open interval $0 < x < 1/(n+1)$ for $n = 0, 1, 2, \ldots$. Show that there is no number which is in all these intervals. How does this relate to Exercise 4?

6. Given that $a_i > 0$ for $i = 0, 1, 2, \ldots$.
   (a)   Show that if $a_0, a_0+a_1, a_0+a_1+a_2, \ldots$ is a Cauchy sequence, then so is $b_0, b_0+b_1, b_0+b_1+b_2, \ldots$, provided that $|b_i| \leq |a_i|$ for $i = 0, 1, 2, \ldots$;

(b)   Show that if a_0, a_0+a_1, $a_0+a_1+a_2$, ... is not a Cauchy sequence, then neither is b_0, b_0+b_1, $b_0+b_1+b_2$, ..., provided that $|b_i| \geq |a_i|$ for $i = 0, 1, 2, \ldots$.

7.   (a)   Show that the sequence 1, $1+1/2!$, $1+1/2!+1/3!$, ... converges by using Exercise 6(a), with $a_i = 1/2^i$ and $b_i = 1/i!$.

     (b)   Show that the sequence 1, $1+1/2$, $1+1/2+1/3$, ... diverges by using Exercise 6(b) with $b_i = 1/(i+1)$ and

$$a_0 = 1,\ a_2 = \tfrac{1}{2},\ a_2 = a_3 = \tfrac{1}{4},$$

$$a_4 = \cdots = a_7 = \tfrac{1}{8}, \ldots,\ a_{2^n} = \cdots = a_{2^{n+1}-1} = \frac{1}{2^{n+1}}$$

8.   (a)   Show that if a_0, a_0+a_1, $a_0+a_1+a_2$, ... is a Cauchy sequence, then $a_n \to 0$.

     (b)   If $r \neq 0$ then 1, r, $2!r^2$, $3!r^3$, ... does not converge. What does item (a) imply about 1, $1+r$, $1+r+2!r^2$, ... ?

     (c)   What do the facts that 1, $1+\tfrac{1}{2}$, $1+\tfrac{1}{2}+\tfrac{1}{3}$, ... is not a convergent sequence and that $1/n \to 0$ imply about (a)?

9.   Many equations have the form $f(x) = x$, where f is a function. A sequence of successive approximations to a solution of this type of equation can sometimes be found by choosing for a_0 any reasonable guess and then constructung $a_1 = f(a_0)$, $a_2 = f(a_1)$, ... Sometimes this sequence is a Cauchy sequence whose limit is a solution of the equation. For instance, suppose that for some a_0 each of the terms $a_1, a_2, \ldots$ constructed in this way is in the domain of f, and suppose that there is a number M, strictly between 0 and 1, such that $|f'(x)| \leq M$ for every x. Show that

     (a) $|a_{i+1}-a_i| \leq M^i|a_1-a_0|$; $i = 0, 1, 2, \ldots$;
     (b) $|a_{n+p}-a_n| \leq |a_1-a_0|M^n/(1-M)$;
     (c) $a_0, a_1, a_2, \ldots$ is a Cauchy sequence;
     (d)   its limit is a solution of the equation $f(x) = x$.

10. Apply the method of Exercise 8 to find a solution correct to two decimal places of $x^2-3x+2 = 0$, using for a_i each of 0, 0.5, 1, 1.5, 2, 2.5. [Hint: Rewrite the equation as $(x^2+2)/3 = x$.]

Infinite Series

If someone travels half of the way from New York to Washington, then half of the remaining distance, then half of the remaining distance, etc., ..., does he eventually reach Washington and if so when? This question is linked with a more numerical one, namely, is it true that $\frac{1}{2}+\frac{1}{4}+\frac{1}{8}+\cdots=1$? This latter question seems to involve an infinite number of additions, and therefore cannot be handled by the usual procedures of arithmetic. Mathematicians have devised a way of dealing with this type of question in terms of sequences and limits of sequences.

DEFINITION: Let a_0, a_1, a_2, ... be an infinite sequence whose terms can be added. Then the ordered pair of sequences consisting of this sequence and the sequence a_0, a_0+a_1, $a_0+a_1+a_2$, ... is called an *infinite series*. The first sequence of this pair is called the *term sequence* of the infinite series, and its terms are called the *terms* of the infinite series. The second sequence of this pair is called the *partial sum sequence* of the infinite series, and its terms are called the *partial sums* of the infinite series.

Notation: An infinite series is denoted by a formal infinite sum $a_0+a_1+a_2+\cdots+a_n+\cdots$, which means the infinite series whose terms sequence is a_0, a_1, a_2, ... and whose partial sum sequence is

$$a_0,\ a_0+a_1,\ a_0+a_1+a_2,\ \ldots.$$

We also use the notation $\sum_{i=0}^{\infty}a_i$ to denote this series. We use some of the abbreviations about signs that we use for finite sums; for instance, we write $1-\frac{1}{2}+\frac{1}{3}-\frac{1}{4}+\cdots$ as an abbreviation for

$$1+(-\tfrac{1}{2})+\tfrac{1}{3}+(-\tfrac{1}{4})+\cdots.$$

Examples:

(a) $\frac{1}{2}+\frac{1}{4}+\frac{1}{8}+\cdots+\frac{1}{2}n+\cdots$ denotes the infinite series whose term sequence is $\frac{1}{2}$, $\frac{1}{4}$, $\frac{1}{8}$, $\cdots$ and whose partial sum sequence is $\frac{1}{2}$, $\frac{3}{4}$, $\frac{7}{8}$, $\ldots$

(b) $1+1+1+\cdots+1+\cdots$ denotes the infinite series whose term sequence is 1, 1, 1, ... and whose partial sum sequence is 1, 2, 3, ...

(c) $1+x+x^2+\cdots+x^{n-1}+\cdots$ denotes the infinite series whose term sequence is 1, x, x^2, ... and whose partial sum sequence is 1, $1+x$ $1+x+x^2$, $\ldots$.

Earlier in this section we asked whether $\frac{1}{2},+\frac{1}{4}+\frac{1}{8}+\cdots$ equals 1 According to our definition, this could not possibly be the case, since the series is a pair of sequences and is not a number. However, we do not wish to define out of existence the conviction that the given series and the given number are intimately related. The next definition supplies the connection.

DEFINITION: The infinite series $a_0+a_1+a_2+\cdots$ is *convergent* and has *sum s* if and only if its sequence of partial sums is convergent and has limit s. An infinite series which is not convergent is said to be *divergent*.

Notation: The sum of the convergent infinite series $a_0+a_1+a_2+\cdots$ is denoted by $S(a_0+a_1+a_2+\cdots)$. The equation $S(a_0+a_1+a_2+\cdots)=s$ means that $a_0+a_1+a_2+\cdots$ converges and has sum s. There is no notation for indicating that $a_0+a_1+a_2+\cdots$ is divergent.

Examples:
(a) $S(\frac{1}{2}+\frac{1}{4}+\frac{1}{8}+\cdots)=1$. This is so because the partial sum sequence of this series is $\frac{1}{2}$, $\frac{3}{4}$, $\frac{7}{8}$, ... which has limit 1.
(b) $S(0.3+0.03+0.003+\cdots)=1/3$. This is so because the partial sum sequence of this series is 0.3, 0.33, 0.333, ... which has limit $1/3$.
(c) The infinite series $1+1+1+\cdots$ is divergent, since its sequence of partial sums is the divergent sequence $1, 2, 3, \ldots$.
(d) The infinite series $1-1+1-1+1-1+\cdots$ is divergent, since its sequence of partial sums is the divergent sequence $1, 0, 1, 0, 1, 0, \cdots$.
(e) The infinite series $1+r+r^2+\cdots$ has sum $1/(1-r)$ if $|r|<1$ and is divergent if $|r|\geq 1$. This is clear if $r=1$. If $r\neq 1$, its partial sum sequence is

$$\frac{1-r}{1-r}, \quad \frac{1-r^2}{1-r}, \quad \frac{1-r^3}{1-r}, \cdots$$

which converges to $1/(1-r)$ if $r<1$ and diverges if $|r|\geq 1$.

THEOREM 5-7: If $a_0+a_1+a_2+\cdots$ is convergent, then its term sequence $a_0, a_1, a_2, \ldots$ converges to 0.

Proof: Denote the partial sum sequence of this series by $b_0, b_1, b_2, \ldots$. Because this is a Cauchy sequence, for $e>0$, where is an N such that $|b_{m+1}-b_m|<e$ if $m>N$. Since $b_{m+1}-b_m=a_{m+1}$, this shows that $a_n\to 0$.

Note: The converse of this theorem is false. The series

$$1+1/2+1/3+\cdots+1/(n+1)+\cdots$$

has $1, 1/2, 1/3, \ldots$ as its term sequence, which converges to 0, but its partial sum sequence diverges. To see this let $b_i=1+1/2+\cdots+1/i$. Then

$$b_{2^{i+1}}-b_{2^i}=\frac{1}{2^i+1}+\frac{1}{2^i+2}+\cdots+\frac{1}{2^{i+1}}.$$

Since each of these summands is at least as large as $1/2^{i+1}$ and since there are 2^i of them, their sum is at least $2^i/2^{i+1} = 1/2$. This shows that the sequence of partial sums of our series is not a Cauchy sequence and therefore does not converge.

Exercises

1. Rewrite in sigma notation:

(a) $1+1+1+\cdots$

(b) $1-1+1-1+\cdots$

(c) $1+\dfrac{1}{3}+\dfrac{1}{3^2}+\cdots$

(d) $1+\dfrac{1}{2}+\dfrac{1}{3}+\dfrac{1}{4}+\cdots$

(e) $1+x+x^2+x^3+\cdots$

(f) $1-x+x^2-x^3+\cdots$

(g) $1-x^2+x^4-x^6+\cdots$

(h) $x-x^3+x^5-x^7+\cdots$

(i) $1+1-1-1+1+1-1-1+\cdots$

2. Find the term sequence and partial sum sequence of each of the series of Exercise 1.

3. Let a_i be an integer from 0 to 9, inclusive, for $i = 1, 2, 3, \ldots$. Show that the infinite series $a_1(0.1)+a_2(0.01)+a_3(0.001)+\cdots$ converges. Discuss $\mathcal{S}(a_1(0.1)+a_2(0.01)+a_3(0.001)+\cdots)$ as a plausible definition for the infinite decimal $0.a_1a_2a_3\ldots$. Do you know any other?

4. (a) Show that every sequence of numbers is the sequence of partial sums for an infinite series.

   (b) Find a relation between term sequences, partial sum sequences, and sequences of first differences.

5. (a) Show that $\mathcal{S}(a_0+a_1+a_2+\cdots)+\mathcal{S}(b_0+b_1+b_2+\cdots)$

$$= \mathcal{S}((a_0+b_0)+(a_1+b_1)+(a_2+b_2)+\cdots).$$

   (b) Show that $\mathcal{S}(ra_0+ra_1+ra_2+\cdots) = r\mathcal{S}(a_0+a_1+a_2+\cdots)$.

6. An infinite series $a_0-a_1+a_2-a_3+\cdots$ is said to be an *alternating* series if $a_0 \geq a_1 \geq a_2 \geq \cdots \geq 0$ and if $a_n \to 0$. Let $b_0, b_1, b_2, \ldots$ be its partial sum sequence. Show that (a) $b_0, b_2, b_4, \ldots$ is monotonically decreasing; (b) $b_1, b_3, b_5, \ldots$ is monotonically increasing; (c) the sequences of (a) and (b) have the same limit s; (d) the series has sum s; (e) $|s-b_n| \leq a_{n+1}$.

7. Use the conclusions of Exercise 6 to show that each of the following converges and to estimate $|s-b_n|$.

(a) $1 - \dfrac{1}{2} + \dfrac{1}{3} - \dfrac{1}{4} + \cdots$

(b) $1 - \dfrac{1}{2!} + \dfrac{1}{3!} - \dfrac{1}{4!} + \cdots$

(c) $1 - \dfrac{1}{3!} + \dfrac{1}{5!} - \dfrac{1}{7!} + \cdots$

8. Find all infinite series whose term sequence $a_0, a_1, a_2, \ldots$ and whose partial sum sequence $b_0, b_1, b_2, \ldots$ satisfy

(a) $a_n = b_n, \quad n = 0, 1, 2, \ldots$

(b) $a_{n+1} = b_n, \quad n = 0, 1, 2, \ldots$

(c) $a_{n+1} = (n+1)b_n, \quad n = 0, 1, 2, \ldots$

9. Find all series $\sum_{i=0}^{\infty} a_i x^i$ such that

(a) $\sum_{i=0}^{\infty} a_i x^i = \sum_{i=0}^{\infty} a_i x^{i-1}$

(b) $\sum_{i=0}^{\infty} a_i x^i = \sum_{i=0}^{\infty} i(i-1)a_i x^{i-2}$

(c) $\sum_{i=0}^{\infty} a_i x^i = \sum_{i=0}^{\infty} -a_i x^{i-1}$

(d) $\sum_{i=0}^{\infty} a_i x^i = \sum_{i=0}^{\infty} -(i)(i-1)a_i x^{i-2}$

10. Show that

(a) $S\left(\dfrac{1}{1 \cdot 2} + \dfrac{1}{2 \cdot 3} + \dfrac{1}{3 \cdot 4} + \cdots \right) = 1$

$$\left[\text{Hint: } \dfrac{1}{n(n+1)} = \dfrac{1}{n} - \dfrac{1}{n+1} \right]$$

(b) $S\left(\dfrac{1}{1 \cdot 2 \cdot 3} + \dfrac{1}{2 \cdot 3 \cdot 4} + \dfrac{1}{3 \cdot 4 \cdot 5} + \cdots \right) = \dfrac{1}{4}$

$$\left[\text{Hint: } \dfrac{1}{n(n+1)(n+2)} = \dfrac{1}{2}\left(\dfrac{1}{n(n+1)} - \dfrac{1}{(n+1)(n+2)} \right) \right]$$

11. It is given about the series $a_0 + a_1 + a_2 + \cdots$ that for every $e > 0$ there is an N such that if $n > N$, then each term of $|a_n|, |a_n + a_{n+1}|, |a_n + a_{n+1} + a_{n+2}|, \ldots$ is less than e. Prove that the sequence of partial sums of the given series is a Cauchy sequence and that the series converges. What is the converse of this assertion? Is it valid?

12. The *remainder after n terms* of the series $\alpha = \sum_{i=0}^{\infty} a_i$ is the series $\beta_n = \sum_{i=n}^{\infty} a_i$. Prove that α converges if and only if each β_n converges and $S(\beta_n) \to 0$.

13. Let $a_0, a_1, a_2, \ldots$ be a sequence of nonzero terms such that $a_{n+1}/a_n \to s$. Prove that $\sum_{i=0}^{\infty} a_i$ converges if $|s| < 1$ and diverges if $|s| > 1$. (Ratio test for convergence.)

Algebra of Power Series

Every function of class $P(t, \infty)$ determines an infinite sequence, its sequence of (t, n) approximations $\sum_{i=0}^{n} a_i(x-t)^i$, $n = 0, 1, 2, \ldots$. This sequence is the partial sum sequence of the infinite series $\sum_{i=0}^{\infty} a_i(x-t)^i$. Such series are an example of an important type of series which we now investigate.

DEFINITION: If t is a number, $a_0, a_1, a_2, \ldots$ a sequence of numbers, and x a variable, then the infinite series $\sum_{i=0}^{\infty} a_i(x-t)^i$ is a *power series* in $x-t$, and t is its *center*.

Notation: Certain abbreviations similar to those used for polynomials are used in denoting power series. These involve 0, 1, minus signs, and parentheses and are all illustrated in the following: $1-x^2+x^4-x^6+\cdots$ is an acceptable abbreviation for

$$1+0(x-0)+(-1)(x-0)^2+0(x-0)^3+\cdots.$$

It is sometimes convenient to regard polynomials in $x-t$ as power series in $x-t$ by agreeing that

$$a_0+a_1(x-t)+\cdots+a_n(x-t)^n$$

is an abbreviation for

$$a_0+a_1(x-t)+\cdots+a_n(x-t)^n+0(x-t)^{n+1}+0(x-t)^{n+2}+\cdots.$$

In particular, we shall meet 0 as an abbreviation for

$$0+0(x-t)+0(x-t)^2+\cdots,$$

we shall meet 1 as an abbreviation for

$$1+0(x-t)+0(x-t)^2+\cdots,$$

and we shall meet x as an abbreviation for

$$t+(x-t)+0(x-t)^2+\cdots.$$

Power series are defined in terms of polynomials, and some of the algebraic properties of these polynomials can be carried over to power series.

DEFINITIONS: Let $\alpha(x)$ be $\sum_{i=0}^{\infty} a_i(x-t)^i$, let $\beta(x)$ be $\sum_{i=0}^{\infty} b_i(x-s)^i$, and let $A_0(x)$, $A_1(x)$, $A_2(x)$, . . . , $B_0(x)$, $B_1(x)$, $B_2(x)$, . . . be their respective partial sum sequences.

(1)   If $t = s$, the *sum* $\alpha(x)+\beta(x)$ is the power series in $x-s$ whose partial sum sequence is $A_n(x)+B_n(x)$, $n = 0, 1, 2, \ldots$.

(2)   If $t = s$, the *product* $\alpha(x)\beta(x)$ is the power series in $x-s$ whose partial sum sequence is the (s, n) product $A_n(x)B_n(x)$, $n = 0, 1, 2, \ldots$.

(3)   If $t = b_0$, the *composite* $\alpha(\beta(x))$ is the power series in $x-s$ whose partial sequence sum is the (s, n) residue of $A_n(B_n(x))$, $n = 0, 1, 2, \ldots$.

Note: It follows from the definition that if $t = s$, then

$$\alpha(x)+\beta(x) = \sum_{i=0}^{\infty} (a_i+b_i)(x-s)^i$$

$$\alpha(x) \cdot \beta(x) = a_0b_0+(a_0b_1-a_1b_0)(x-s)+(a_0b_2+a_1b_1+a_2b_0)(x-s)^2+ \cdots$$

We cannot form $\alpha(\beta(x))$ unless $t = b_0$. The coefficients c_i in the resulting series $\sum_{i=0}^{\infty} c_i(x-s)^i$ have no simple formula in terms of the a_i and b_i. Recall that Lemma 2-13 describes c_i as $a_1b_i+a_ib_i{}^i+W_i$, where W_i is a polynomial in $a_2, \ldots, a_{i-1}, b_1, \ldots, b_{i-1}$.

Examples:

(a)   If $\alpha(x) = 1+x+x^2+ \cdots$ and if $\beta(x) = 1-x+x^2- \cdots$, then $\alpha(x)+\beta(x) = 2+2x^2+2x^4+ \cdots$, and $\alpha(x) \cdot \beta(x) = 1+x^2+x^4+ \cdots$.

(b)   If $\alpha(x) = 1+x+x^2+ \cdots$, and if $\beta(x) = x-x^2+x^3+ \cdots$, then $A_1(B_1(x))$, $A_2(B_2(x))$, . . . , $A_n(B_n(x))$, . . . all reduce to $1+x$. Therefore, $\alpha(\beta(x)) = 1+x$.

Each of the three operations just defined suggests an appropriate inverse operation.

DEFINITIONS: Let $\alpha(x)$ and $\beta(x)$ be power series.

(1)   If $\alpha(x)+\beta(x) = 0$, we say that $\alpha(x)$ and $\beta(x)$ are *negatives* of one another and write $\alpha(x) = -\beta(x)$, $\beta(x) = -\alpha(x)$.

(2)   If $\alpha(x) \cdot \beta(x) = 1$, we say that $\alpha(x)$ and $\beta(x)$ are *reciprocals* of one another and write $\alpha(x) = 1/\beta(x)$, $\beta(x) = 1/\alpha(x)$.

(3)   If $\alpha(\beta(x)) = x$ and if $\beta(\alpha(x)) = x$, we say that $\alpha(x)$ and $\beta(x)$ are *inverses* of one another and write $\alpha(x) = \beta^{-1}(x)$, $\beta(x) = \alpha^{-1}(x)$.

Note: In (1) above, 0 means the series $0+0(x-s)+0(x-s)^2+ \cdots$. In (2) above, 1 means the series $1+0(x-s)+0(x-s)^2+ \cdots$. In (3) above, $\alpha(\beta(x)) = x$ means that $\alpha(\beta(x)) = s + (x-s) + 0(x-s)^2 + \cdots$, and $\beta(\alpha(x)) = x$ means $\beta(\alpha(x)) = t + (x-t) + 0(x-t)^2 + \cdots$.

THEOREM 5-8: Let $\alpha(x)$ be the series $\sum a_i(x-t)^i$; then

(1) $\alpha(x)$ has a unique negative;

(2) $\alpha(x)$ has a reciprocal if and only if $a_0 \neq 0$ and if it has one it is unique.

(3) $\alpha(x)$ has an inverse if and only if $a_1 \neq 0$ and if it has one it is unique.

Proof: The proof follows immediately from Theorems 2-10 and 2-16.

Examples:

(a) If $\alpha(x) = 1 + x + x^2 + \cdots$, then

(1) $-\alpha(x) = -1 - x - x^2 - \cdots$

(2) $1/\alpha(x) = 1 - x$

(3) $\alpha^{-1}(x) = (x-1) - (x-1)^2 + (x-1)^3 - \cdots$

(b) If $\alpha(x) = 1 + x + x^2/2! + x^3/3! + \cdots$, then

(1) $-\alpha(x) = -1 - x - x^2/2! - x^3/3! - \cdots$

(2) $1/\alpha(x) = 1 - x + x^2/2! - x^3/3! + \cdots$

(3) $\alpha^{-1}(x) = x - 1 - (x-1)^2/2 + (x-1)^3/3 - \cdots$

The operations on power series that were just defined can sometimes be useful in the study of sequences of numbers. An example will show how this happens, after a preliminary definition.

DEFINITION: If $a_0, a_1, a_2, \ldots$ is any sequence of numbers, then the power series $a_0 + a_1 x + a_2 x^2 + \cdots$ is its *generating* series.

Problem: The conditions $a_0 = 1$, $a_1 = 1$, $a_{n+2} = a_{n+1} + 2a_n$ for $n = 0, 1, 2, \ldots$ determine the sequence $1, 1, 3, 5, 11, 21, \ldots$. It is required to express a_n algebraically in terms of n.

Solution: Let $\alpha(x) = a_0 + a_1 x + a_2 x^2 + \cdots$ be the generating series for the sequence. Then $x\alpha(x) = a_0 x + a_1 x^2 + \cdots$ and $x^2 \alpha(x) = a_0 x^2 + a_1 x^3 \cdots$. Therefore,

$$\alpha(x) - x\alpha(x) - 2x^2 \alpha(x) = 1 + 0x + 0x^2 + \cdots = 1.$$

We conclude that $\alpha(x) = 1/(1-x-2x^2)$. To find the reciprocal of $1+x-x^2$ (regarded as a power series), write

$$\frac{1}{1-x-2x^2} = \frac{1}{(1-2x)(1+x)} = \left(\frac{1}{3}\right)\frac{1}{1+x} + \left(\frac{2}{3}\right)\frac{1}{1-2x}$$

$$= \tfrac{1}{3}(1-x+x^2+\cdots) + \tfrac{2}{3}(1+2x+4x^2+\cdots)$$

$$= 1+x+3x^2+\cdots + ((\tfrac{1}{3})(-1)^n + (\tfrac{2}{3})2^n)\,x^n + \cdots.$$

We conclude that

$$a_n = (\tfrac{1}{3})(-1)^n + (\tfrac{2}{3})2^n.$$

Exercises

1. Find all power series $\alpha(x)$ such that
   (a) $\alpha(-x) = -\alpha(x)$;
   (b) $\alpha(-x) = \alpha(x)$.

2. Find the reciprocal of each and check your answer by multiplication.

   (a) $\sum x^n$; (b) $\sum(-1)^n x^n$; (c) $\sum(n+1)x^n$; (d) $\sum \frac{1}{n+1} x^{n+1}$
   (e) $1+ax$.

3. Verify that $\dfrac{2+x}{1+x-6x^2} = \dfrac{1}{1-2x} + \dfrac{1}{1+3x}$, first by ordinary algebra and then by regarding the polynomials as power series.

4. If $\alpha(x) = \sum(n+1)x^n$, find $\alpha(x)^2$, $\alpha(x)^3$, $\alpha(x)^m$.

5. Given that $\sum a_i(x+y)^i = (\sum a_i x^i)(\sum a_i y^i)$ and $a_0 = 1$, find $a_1, a_2, \ldots$.

6. Find all power series $P(x)$ such that
   (a) $P(x)^2 = 1+x$
   (b) $P(x)^3 = 1+x$
   (c) $P(x)^n = 1+x$ if n is any positive integer
   (d) $P(x)^n = 1+x$ if n is a negative integer

7. Let r be any number and let $P(x, r)$ be

$$1 + \frac{r}{1}x + \frac{r(r-1)}{1\cdot 2}x^2 + \cdots + \frac{r(r-1)\cdots(r-i+1)}{i!}x^i + \cdots.$$

Show that (a) $P(x, r) = (1+x)^r$ if r is a positive integer

          (b) $P(x, r)$ is the reciprocal of $(1+x)^{-r}$ if r is a negative integer

          (c) $(1+x)P(x, r) = P(x, r+1)$ no matter what kind of number r is

8.   Let $s(x) = x - \dfrac{x^3}{3!} + \dfrac{x^3}{5!} - \cdots$ and let $c(x) = 1 - \dfrac{x^2}{2!} + \dfrac{x^4}{4!} + \cdots$. Prove that

    (a) $s(x)^2 + c(x)^2 = 1$;

    (b) $s(2x) = 2s(x)c(x)$;

    (c) $c(2x) = c(x)^2 - s(x)^2$.

9.   If $P(x)$ is the power series $\sum_{i=0}^{\infty} a_i x^i$, its formal derivative $P(x)'$ is the power series $\sum_{i=0}^{\infty} i a_i x^{i-1}$.

    (a)   Show that

$$(P(x) + Q(x))' = P(x)' + Q(x)',$$
$$(P(x)Q(x))' = P(x)Q(x)' + P(x)'Q(x),$$
$$(P(x)^r)' = rP(x)^{r-1}P(x)' \quad (r \text{ is a positive integer}),$$
$$(1/P(x))' = -P(x)^2 P(x)'.$$

    (b)   Find all power series $P(x)$ if

$$P(x)' = P(x), \qquad\qquad P(x)'' + P(x) = 0,$$
$$P(x)' = cP(x), \qquad\qquad P(x)'' + cP(x) = 0,$$
$$P(x)' = xP(x), \qquad\qquad P(x)'' - 3P(x)' + 2P(x) = 0.$$

10.   A *generalized power* series is a series of the form

$$a_{-n}x^{-n} + a_{-n+1}x^{-n+1} + \cdots + a_{-1}x^{-1} + \sum_{i=0}^{\infty} a_i x^i$$

where n is a nonnegative integer and $a_{-n}, \ldots, a_{-n}$ are numbers.

    (a)   Define multiplication of such series.

    (b)   Show that if $P(x)$ is any nonzero power series, then there is a generalized power series such that $P(x)Q(x) = 1$.

    (c)   Show that if $P(x)$ and $R(x)$ are any generalized power series, then there is a generalized power series $R(x)$ such that $P(x) \cdot Q(x) = R(x)$.

11.   The Fibonacci numbers are defined by the rule $a_0 = 1$, $a_1 = 1$, $a_{n+2} = a_{n+1} + a_n$ for $n \geq 0$. Find an explicit formula for a_n by finding the generating series $P(x)$ of the sequence. [Hint: Show first that $P(x) = 1(/1 - x - x^2)$. Show next that

$$\frac{1}{1 - x - x^2} = \frac{1}{\sqrt{5}}\left(\frac{r}{1 - rx} - \frac{s}{1 - sx}\right),$$

where
$$r = \frac{1+\sqrt{5}}{2}, \qquad s = \frac{1-\sqrt{5}}{2}.$$

Use this to conclude that
$$a_n = (1\sqrt{5})(r^{n+1} - s^{n+1}).$$

12. Show by direct substitution that if $A(x) = 1/(1-x)$ and $B(x) = (x-1)/x$, then $A(B(x)) = x$ and $B(A(x)) = x$. Find a power series version of these relations.

13. Find $A(B(x))$ if
(a) $A(x) = B(x) = x + x^2 + x^3 + \cdots$;
(b) $A(x) = x + x^2/2 + \cdots + x^n/n! + \cdots$,
$B(x) = x - x^2/2 + \cdots + (-1)^{n-1}x^n/n + \cdots$;
(c) $A(x) = x + x^2/2 + \cdots + x^n/n + \cdots$,
$B(x) = -x - x^2/2 - \cdots - x^n/n! \cdots$.

14. Find the inverse of (a) $x + x^2$; (b) $x + x^2 + x^3$; (c) $x + x^2 + \cdots + x^n + \cdots$; (d) $x + 2x^2 + 3x^3 + \cdots$.

15. Show that
$$x - \frac{x^3}{3!} + \frac{x^5}{5!} - \cdots \quad \text{and} \quad x + \frac{1x^3}{2\cdot3} + \frac{1\cdot3}{2\cdot4}\frac{x^5}{5} + \frac{1\cdot3\cdot5}{2\cdot4\cdot6}\frac{x^7}{7} + \cdots$$

are inverses.

16. If $A(x) = a_1x + a_2x^2 + \cdots$ with $a_1 \neq 0$, if $B(x) = b_1x + b_2x^2 + \cdots$, with $b_1 \neq 0$, and if $A(B(x)) = x$, must $B(A(x)) = x$?

CHAPTER 6

Functions Defined by Power Series

It has been shown how polynomials define functions, and these functions have been investigated by investigation of the polynomials that define them. We turn now to a more extensive class of functions defined by similar but more elaborate expressions, namely, power series. Early users of power series treated them very much like polynomials. They did not worry about whether or not their series converged, and they did not distinguish between operations on the series and operations on the functions defined by the series. However, they soon discovered that certain precautions had to be taken if working with series was not to lead to nonsense. (Some of the situations which call for caution are listed in Appendix A.) This need for caution has become part of the collective mathematical conscience, and students sometimes are given false impression that series are too tricky to be useful. It is hoped that the point of view that emerges from this exposition is a bolder one, namely, that whenever a formula is needed for almost anything, it is reasonable to look for it in the form of a series, and that the search for the formula can be more pleasant than perilous.

Interval of Convergence

Every power series $\alpha(x)$ defines a function, namely, the one whose domain is the set of values at which $\alpha(x)$ converges and whose value at each such s is $S(\alpha(x))$. This is called the *sum function* of $\alpha(x)$. Sum functions arise in many mathematical investigations, and their theory is a fundamental one. We begin it now.

THEOREM 6-1: If $\sum a_i x^i$ converges at R, where $R \neq 0$, then it also converges at every s in the interval $|x| < |R|$.

Proof. Because the term sequence of $\sum a_i R^i$ has limit 0, it is bounded, and there is a number M such that $|a_i R^i| < M$ for $i = 0, 1, 2, \ldots$. This fact is used to show that the term sequence $A_0(s), A_1(s), A_2(s), \ldots$ of $\sum a_i s^i$ is a Cauchy sequence. If $m > n$, we have

$$|A_m(s) - A_n(s)| = |a_{n+1} s^{n+1} + \cdots + a_m s^m|$$

$$\leq |a_{n+1} s^{n+1}| + \cdots + |a_m s^m|$$

$$\leq M|s/R|^{n+1} + \cdots + |M| |s/R|^n$$

$$= \frac{M|s/R|^{n+1}(1 - |s/R|^{m-n})}{1 - |s/R|}$$

Since $|s/R| < 1$, this expression is less than or equal to

$$\frac{M|s/R|^{n+1}}{1 - |s/R|}$$

which, according to Corollary 5-3, has limit zero. We see that $A_0(s)$, $A_1(s), A_2(s), \ldots$ is indeed a Cauchy sequence and $\sum a_i s^i$ converges.

COROLLARY 6-2: If for some R the terms of $\sum a_i R^i$ are bounded, then, even if this series is divergent, the series $\sum a_i s^i$ converges if $|s| < |R|$.

COROLLARY 6-3:

$$|S(\sum a_i s^i) - A_n^{(s)}| < \frac{M|s/R|^{n+1}}{1 - |s/R|}$$

COROLLARY 6-4: The series $|a_0| + |a_1 s| + |a_2 s^2| + \cdots$ is convergent, and its partial sums $|a_0| + |a_1 s| + \cdots + |a_n s^n|$ differ from its sum, in absolute value, by less than $(|Ms/R|^{n+1})/(1 - |s/R|)$.

We conclude that if $\alpha(x)$ is a power series in x, then either.

(1) $\alpha(x)$ converges only at 0;

(2) $\alpha(x)$ converges for every x;

(3) there is a number R such that $\alpha(x)$ converges at x if $|x| < R$ and diverges at x if $|x| > R$.

The number R of case (3) is called the *radius of convergence* of $\alpha(x)$. The other cases are often described in similar language—the "radius of convergence" in case (1) is said to be zero, and that in the case (2) is said to be infinite.

Examples:

(a) The *geometric series* $1+x+x^2+\cdots$ has radius of convergence equal to 1. This is so because its term sequence is bounded at 1, unbounded at x if $|x|>1$.

(b) The series $1+x+x^2/2!+\cdots+x^n/n!+\cdots$ converges at every x (has an infinite radius of convergence). To see that it converges at x, choose an integer N greater than $|x|$, and infer from

$$\frac{x^{n+p}}{(N+p)!}=\frac{x^N}{N!}\frac{x^p}{(N+1)\cdots(N+p)} \quad \text{that} \quad \left|\frac{x^{N+p}}{(N+p)!}\right|\leq\frac{x^N}{N!}$$

$p=1,2,\ldots$. This shows that the term sequence is bounded for every x. (Note that the timing is important in this argument—first the x must be given, then the N is chosen.)

(c) $1+x+(2!)x^2+(3!)x^3+\cdots$ diverges at every x other than 0. To see this, choose an N for which $N>|2/x|$. Then

$$|(N+p)!x^{N+p}|=|(N!)x^N(N+1)\cdots(N+p)x^p|\geq|(N!)x^N|2^p.$$

This shows that the term sequence of the given series is unbounded.

These facts about the convergence of power series in x can be translated readily into similar facts about power series in $x-t$, and we do so freely in what follows. For instance, Example (a) implies that $1+(x-3)+(x-3)^2+\cdots$ converges if $|x-3|<1$, and that it diverges if $|x-3|>1$. Example (b) implies that $1+(x+2)+(x+2)^2/2!+\cdots+(x+2)^n/n!+\cdots$ converges at every value of x. Example (c) implies that $1+(x-5)+2!(x-5)^2+\cdots+n!(x-5)^n+\cdots$ diverges at x if $x\neq5$. Note that our error estimate for power series at $x-t$ is

$$M\frac{\left|\dfrac{s-t}{R-t}\right|^{n+1}}{1-\left|\dfrac{s-t}{R-t}\right|}.$$

Definition: If a power series $\alpha(x)$ in $x-t$ converges for a value of x other than t, we say that its sum function f is *analytic*, and that $\alpha(x)$

is the *Taylor series expansion* of f with *center* t. If $t = 0$, we also say that $\alpha(x)$ is the *MacLaurin series expansion* of f.

If R is the radius of convergence of $\sum a_i(x-t)^i$, we know that the series converges at x if $|x-t| < R$, and that it diverges at x if $|x-t| > R$. This does not say anything about convergence at $t+R$ or $t-R$ and, in fact, no general conclusion can be drawn about convergence at these values. For example, consider

$$(1) \quad 1+x+x^2+ \cdots +x^n+ \cdots ;$$

$$(2) \quad 1+\frac{x}{2}+\frac{x^2}{3}+ \cdots +\frac{x^n}{n+1}+ \cdots ;$$

$$(3) \quad 1-\frac{x}{2}+\frac{x^2}{3}+ \cdots +\frac{(-1)^n x^n}{n+1}+ \cdots ;$$

$$(4) \quad 1-\frac{x^2}{2}+\frac{x^4}{3}+ \cdots +\frac{(-1)^n x^{2n}}{n+1}+ \cdots .$$

For each we have $t = 0$ and $R = 1$. The first clearly diverges at 1 and at -1, since its term sequence does not converge to zero at these values. The series (2) converges at -1, diverges at 1; the series (3) converges at 1, diverges at -1; the series (4) converges at 1 and at -1. These assertions about (2), (3), and (4) follow from the facts that at 1 and -1 each series is either the (divergent) harmonic series $1+\frac{1}{2}+\frac{1}{3}+ \cdots$ or the (convergent) alternating series $1-\frac{1}{2}+\frac{1}{3}- \cdots$.

If a power series in $x-t$ converges for $|x-t| < R$ and diverges for $|x-t| > R$, the open interval $|x-t| < R$ is called the *interval of convergence* of the series. Hence, the behavior of the series at $t+R$ and $t-R$ does not enter into the specification of the interval of convergence

It often happens that the sum of an infinite series cannot be found exactly and that a partial sum is used as an approximation to this sum. In the case of power series, the expression $(M|s/R|^{n+1})/(1-|s/R|)$ is available then to estimate the error involved.

Example: If $\alpha(x) = 1+x+x^2+ \cdots$, we might wish to know how reliable $1+\frac{1}{3}+\frac{1}{3^2}+ \cdots +\frac{1}{3^n}$ is as an estimate for $\mathcal{S}\left(1+\frac{1}{3}+\frac{1}{3^2}+ \cdots \right)$. Since $M = 1$, $R = 1$, $s = \frac{1}{3}$, we compute $(\frac{1}{3})^{n+1}/(1-(\frac{1}{3}))$ or $\frac{1}{2}(\frac{1}{3})^n$ as a bound for the error. This fact can be used in two ways. It says, for instance, that if $n = 3$ the error is no greater than $1/54$. If the permissable error is specified, it can also be used to find a value of n which will meet that standard. For instance, if the error must not exceed 0.0000001, then the smallest n for which $\frac{1}{2}(\frac{1}{3})^n < 0.0000001$ can be computed and the partial sum corresponding to this value can be depended on to be in error by less than the amount specified.

For any given value of n the expression for the error estimate decreases as $|s-t|$ decreases. This has the useful implication that if the error estimate for certain values s and n falls within the limits permitted by the conditions of the problem, then for every x for which $|x-t| < |s-t|$ the same conclusion can be drawn. This is sometimes expressed by the statement that convergent power series converge *uniformly* in every closed interval in which they converge.

Exercises

1. (Ratio test)   Suppose that M is a number, $a_0, a_1, a_2, \ldots$ is a sequence.

   (a) If $|a_{i+1}/a_i| \leq M$ for every i greater than some integer N, show that the series $\sum_{i=0}^{\infty} a_i x^i$ converges for $|x| < 1/M$ by showing that its term sequence is bounded at these values of x.

   (b) If $|a_{i+1}/a_i| \geq M$ for every i greater than some integer N, show that the series $\sum_{i=0}^{\infty} a_i x^i$ diverges for $|x| > 1/M$ by showing that its term sequence does not converge to 0 for these values of x.

   (c) Use this test to find the interval of convergence of each of the following series.

   $1 + x + x^2 + \cdots$

   $1 - x + x^2 - \cdots$

   $1 + x + x^2/2 + \cdots + x^n/n! + \cdots$

   $1 - x + x^2/2 + \cdots + (-1)^n x^n/n! + \cdots$

   $1 + x^2 + x^4 + \cdots + x^{2n} + \cdots$

   $1 + x^2/2! + \cdots + x^{2n}/(2n!) + \cdots$

   $x + x^2/2 + \cdots + x^n/n + \cdots$

   $x + 2x^2 + \cdots + nx^n + \cdots$

   $1 + (x-3) + (x-3)^2 + \cdots + (x-3)^n + \cdots$

   $1 + (x+5)^2 + (x+5)^4 + \cdots + (x+5)^n + \cdots$

   $1 + (x-5) + (x-5)^2/2! + \cdots + (x-5)^n/n! + \cdots$

   (d) For each of the series of part (c) find an estimate for the remainder after n-terms.

Analytic Functions

With every function f of class $P(t, \infty)$ there is associated a power series in $x-t$, namely, the one whose partial sum sequence is the sequence of (t, n) approximation to f. This association is complicated by two facts: (a) the associated power series need not converge for any x other than t; (b) the associated power series can converge and have a sum function different from f. However, there are significant connections between sum functions of power series in $x-t$ and functions of class $P(t, \infty)$, and we study these now.

THEOREM 6-5: Let $\alpha(x)$ be $a_0+a_1(x-t)+a_2(x-t)^2+\cdots$, and suppose that $\alpha(x)$ converges for at least one x_0 other than t. Then the sum function of $\alpha(x)$ is of class $P(t, \infty)$ and its (t, n) approximation is $a_0+a_1(x-t)+\cdots+a_n(x-t)^n$, for $n = 0, 1, 2, \ldots$.

Proof: Let M be an upper bound for the term sequence of $a_0+a_1(x_0-t)$, $a_2(x_0-t)^2+\cdots$, and let $B_n(x)$ be $a_0+a_1(x-t)+\cdots+a_n(x-t)^n$. Then, if $|x-t| < |x_0-t|$, we have

$$|\mathcal{S}(\alpha(x))-B_n(x)| \leq \frac{M\left|\dfrac{x-t}{x_0-t}\right|^{n+1}}{1-\left|\dfrac{x-t}{x_0-t}\right|}.$$

If we require that $|x-t| < \frac{1}{2}|x_0-t|$, then the expression on the right is less than $M'|x-t|^{n+1}$ where $M' = 2M/(|x_0-t|^{n+1})$. This shows that $\mathcal{S}(\alpha(x))-B_n(x)$ has order n at t for $n = 0, 1, 2, \ldots$.

COROLLARY 6-6: If $\sum a_i(x-t)^i$ converges for a value of x other than t and if f is its sum function, then $a_0 = f(t)$, and $a_1 = f'(t)$.

LEMMA 6-7: If $\alpha(x) = a_0+a_1x+a_2x^2+\cdots$ converges at s, then $\beta(x) = a_m+a_{m+1}x+\cdots+a_{m+r}x^r+\cdots$ converges at s, for $m = 1, 2, 3, \ldots$.

Proof. Denote by $B_0(x), B_1(x), B_2(x), \ldots$ the partial sum sequence of $\alpha(x)$. Then the partial sum sequence of $\beta(x)$ is

$$\frac{B_{m+r}(x)-B_{m-1}(x)}{x^m}, \qquad \text{for } r = 1, 2, 3, \ldots.$$

Since the first sequence has limit $S(\alpha(x_0))$ at x_0 the second has limit

$$\frac{S(\alpha(x_0)) - B_{m-1}(x_0)}{x_0{}^m} \quad \text{at } x_0.$$

LEMMA 6-8: Let $\alpha(x)$ be $a_0 + a_1 x + a_2 x^2 + \cdots$ and let $t_0, t_1, t_2, \ldots$ be an infinite sequence of nonzero numbers such that $t_n \to 0$. If $S(\alpha(t_n)) = 0$ for $n = 0, 1, 2, \ldots$, then $a_n = 0$ for $n = 0, 1, 2, \ldots$.

Proof: Suppose the statement is false. Then there is an integer m such that $a_m \neq 0$ and $a_0 = a_1 = \cdots = a_{m-1} = 0$. Combining this with Lemma 6-7 and our hypothesis $S(\alpha(t_i)) = 0$, we have $S(a_m + a_{m+1} t_i + a_{m+2} t_i{}^2 + \cdots) = 0$ for $i = 0, 1, 2, \ldots$. But we also know from Theorem 6-5 that the sum function $S(\alpha(x))$ of $a_m + a_{m+1} x + a_{m+2} x^2 + \cdots$ is continuous at $x = 0$ and has the value a_m there. Since $a_m \neq 0$, it follows that there is a number d such that if $|x| < d$ then $S(\alpha(x)) \neq 0$. Since our hypothesis implies that there is a t_i for which $|t_i| < d$ and $S(\alpha(t_i)) = 0$, we have a contradiction.

This lemma resembles the theorem for polynomials which says that only the zero polynomial is zero for an infinite number of values. For polynomials, however, there is no restriction on the convergence of these values, and for power series such a condition is essential. In fact, we shall see later that $\sin x$ is defined by the power series

$$\sum_{i=0}^{\infty} \frac{(-1)^{2n+1} x^{2n+1}}{(2n+1)!}$$

and we know that $\sin(n\pi) = 0$; $n = 0, 1, 2, \ldots$. This shows that a power series equation $S(P(x)) = 0$ can have an infinite number of solutions in cases where $P(x)$ is not the zero power series.

THEOREM 6-9 (Identity Theorem): Let $\alpha(x)$ be $a_0 + a_1 x + a_2 x^2 + \cdots$, let $\beta(x)$ be $b_0 + b_1 x + b_2 x^2 + \cdots$, and let $t_0, t_1, t_2, \ldots$ be a sequence of nonzero numbers such that $t_n \to 0$. If $S(\alpha(t_n)) = S(\beta(t_n))$ for $n = 0, 1, 2, \ldots$, then $a_n = b_n$ for $n = 0, 1, 2, \ldots$ and $S(\alpha(x)) = S(\beta(x))$ for every x at which the series converge.

Proof: Apply Lemma 6-8 to $\alpha(x) - \beta(x)$ and use the fact that $S(\alpha(x) - \beta(x)) = S(\alpha(x)) - S(\beta(x))$.

We have seen that the function defined by the polynomial $\sum_{i=0}^{n} a_i(x-t)^i$ is differentiable and that its derivative is defined by the polynomial $\sum_{i=1}^{n} ia_i(x-t)^{i-1}$. A corresponding fact holds for functions defined by power series, namely, that if $\sum_{i=0} a_i(x-t)^i$ converges to $f(x)$ in some interval, then f must be differentiable, and the series $\sum_{i=0}^{\infty} ia_i(x-t)^{i-1}$, obtained by "differentiating term by term," converges to $f'(x)$ for every x in the interval. We establish this fact and explore some of its consequences now.

LEMMA 6-10: If $0 \le r < 1$, then the sequence $nr^{n-1}, n = 1, 2, 3, \ldots,$ is bounded.

Proof: Since $n/(n+1) \to 1$, we can choose N so large that $n/(n+1) > r$ if $n > N$. Since the successor of each term of the sequence is obtainable by multiplying it by $r(n+1)/n$, if $n > N$ the terms are decreasing. Thus the largest of $1, 2r, \ldots, Nr^{N-1}$, is an upper bound for the sequence. Zero is clearly a lower bound.

LEMMA 6-11: If b is the greater of $|x|$ and $|t|$, then

$$|x^n - t^n - nt^{n-1}(x-t)| \le n(n-1)b^{n-2}|x-t|^2.$$

Proof: According to Taylor's Theorem,

$$x^n = t^n + nt^{n-1}(x-t) + n(n-1)c^{n-2}(x-t)_2^2$$

where c is between x and t. Since $|n(n-1)c^{n-2}(x-t)^2|$ is less than or equal to $n(n-1)b^{n-2}|x-t|^2$, the result follows.

LEMMA 6-12: The series $\sum_{i=0}^{\infty} a_i x^i$ and $\sum_{i=0}^{\infty} ia_i x^{i-1}$ have the same interval of convergence.

Proof: Let I be the interval of convergence of $\sum_{i=0}^{\infty} a_i x^{i-1}$, and let r be any point in I. We show that $\sum_{i=0}^{\infty} ia_i r^{i-1}$ converges. Because I is open, we can find an R_1 and an R_2 in I, with $R_1 > R_2 > |r|$. Because $\sum_{i=0}^{\infty} a_i R_1^i$ converges, the sequence $a_i R_1^i$ is bounded. We show that the sequence $ia_i R_2^{i-1}$ is bounded. We have

$$ia_i R_2^{i-1} = a_i R_1^i \frac{i}{R_1} \left(\frac{R_2}{R_1}\right)^{i-1}$$

If 1 is an upper bound for $a_i R_1^i$ and if M_2 is an upper bound for $i(R_2/R_1)^{i-1}$, then $(M_1 M_2)/R_1$ is an upper bound for $ia_i R_2^{i-1}$. Since $|r| < R_2$, it follows that $\sum_{i=1}^{\infty} ia_i r^{i-1}$ converges. Conversely, it is clear that if the sequence $ia_i r^{i-1}$ is bounded, so is $a_i r^i$. The result follows.

COROLLARY 6-13:   For every positive integer k the series

$$\sum_{i=k}^{\infty} (i(i-1) \cdots (i-k+1)a_i\, x^{i-k}$$

has the same interval of convergence as $\sum_{i=0}^{\infty} a_i\, x^i$.

Proof.   Apply the lemma k times.

COROLLARY 6-14:   The series $\sum_{i=0}^{\infty} a_i x^i$ and $\sum_{i=0}^{\infty} (a_i/(i+1))x^{i+1}$ have the same interval of convergence.

Proof.   The first series is obtained from the second by term-by-term differentiation.

THEOREM 6-15:   If $\sum_{i=0}^{\infty} a_i x^i$ converge for every x in the interval $(-d, d)$, then its sum function f is differentiable and $\sum_{i=0}^{\infty} ia_i\, x^{i-1}$ converges to $f'(x)$ for every x in this interval.

Proof.   We are to show that if t is in $(-d, d)$, then

$$S\left(\sum_{i=0}^{\infty} a_i\, x^i\right) - S\left(\sum_{i=0}^{\infty} a_i\, t^i\right) - S\left(\sum_{i=0}^{\infty} ia_i\, t^{i-1}\right)(x-t)$$

has order one at t. Since each of the three series in this expression converges if x is also in $(-d, d)$, this expression is the sum of the series

$$\sum_{i=0}^{\infty} a_i(x^i - t^i - it^{i-1}(x-t)).$$

According to Lemma 6-10, each term of this series has absolute value no greater than that of the corresponding term of the series $\sum_{i=0}^{\infty} i(i-1)a_i\, b^{i-2}(x-t)^2$. By invoking Corollary 6-13, with $k = 2$, and the comparison test for convergence, we see that our expression is dominated at t by $S(\sum_{i=0}^{\infty} i(i-1)a_i\, b^{i-2})(x-t)^2$. Since this has order 1 at t, the result follows.

COROLLARY 6-16:   If $\sum_{i=0}^{\infty} a_i(x-t)^i$ converges for every x in the interval $(t-d, t+d)$, then its sum function f is differentiable and $\sum_{i=0}^{\infty} ia_i(x-t)^{i-1}$ converges to $f'(x)$ for every x in this interval.

COROLLARY 6-17:   If $\sum_{i=0}^{\infty} a_i(x-t)^i$ converges for every x in the interval $(t-d, t+d)$ then, for every positive integer k, its sum function f has a derivative of order k and $\sum_{i=0}^{\infty} i(i-1) \ldots (i-k+1)a_i(x-t)^{i-k}$ converges to $f^{(k)}(x)$ for every x in this interval.

C="COROLLARY" 6-18: If $f(x) = S(\sum_{i=0}^{\infty} a_i(x-t)^i)$, then $a_k = f^{(k)}(t)/k!$, for $k = 0, 1, 2, \ldots$.

COROLLARY 6-19: If $f(x) = S(\sum_{i=0}^{\infty} a_i(x-t)^i)$, then

$$S\left(\sum_{i=0}^{\infty} \frac{a_i}{i+1}(x-t)^{i+1}\right)$$

is an antiderivative of f.

Examples:

(a) $1+x+x^2+\cdots$ converges to $1/(1-x)$ for $|x| < 1$. It follows that $1+2x+3x^2+\cdots$ converges to its derivative $1/(1-x)^2$ for $|x| < 1$. It also follows that $x+x^2/2+x^3/3+\cdots$ converges to $\int 1/(1-x)$ for $|x| < 1$. (This antiderivative will be identified and studied in Chapter 7.)

(b) $1+x+x^2/2!+x^3/3!+\cdots$ converges for every x. This series has the property that it is the same as the series obtained from it by term-by-term differentiation. It follows that the function it defines is its own derivative. This function will be identified and studied in Chapter 7.)

In our study of functions we have introduced the properties "class $P(t, \infty)$", "infinitely differentiable," and "analytic." We have seen that if a function is infinitely differentiable in an interval, then it is of class $P(t, \infty)$ for every t in that interval. We have just seen that if a function is analytic in an interval, then it is infinitely differentiable in the interval. Those results suggest the converse questions, "Is every function of class $P(t, \infty)$ infinitely differentiable?" "Is every infinitely differentiable function analytic?" The answer turns out to be "no" in each case. The next theorem states conditions on infinitely differentiable functions which guarantee that they are analytic.

THEOREM 6-20: Suppose the function f is infinitely differentiable for every x in the interval $(t-R, t+R)$ and that there is a number M such that $\left|\dfrac{f^{(n)}(s)}{n!} R^n\right| \leq M$ for every s in this interval and for $n = 1, 2,$ $3, \ldots$. Then the series $\sum_{i=0}^{\infty} \dfrac{f^{(i)}(t)}{i!}(x-t)^i$ converges to $f(x)$ for $|x-t| < R$.

Proof: Let $\beta_n(x)$ be the n-th partial sum of the series proposed for f.

According to Taylor's Theorem, if $|x-t| < R$, then $f(x) - \beta_n(x) = \dfrac{f^{(n)}(c_n)}{n!}(x-t)^n$, where c_n is between x and t, for $n = 1, 2, 3, \ldots$

Therefore,

$$f(x) - \beta_n(x) = \frac{f^{(n)}(c_n)}{n!} R^n \left(\frac{x-t}{R}\right)^n$$

whence

$$|f(x) - \beta_n(x)| \leq M \left|\frac{x-t}{R}\right|^n.$$

Since the terms on the right approach zero as n becomes infinite, we infer that $\beta_n(x) \to f(x)$. But it is clear from Corollary 6-2 that the proposed series converges for $|x-t| < R$. Since its sum is, by definition, $\lim\limits_{n \to \infty} \beta_n(x)$, the result follows.

COROLLARY 6-21: If f is differentiable for $|x-t| < R$ and if $f' = f$ in this interval, then f is analytic.

Proof: It is easy to see that f is of class $P(s, \infty)$ for every s in the interval. In fact $(f'') = (f')' = (f)' = f$, $(f''') = (f'')' = f, \ldots$, so f has derivatives of all orders at every s. It is therefore of class $P(s, \infty)$ at every s. Because f is continuous, it is bounded on the given closed interval. Since the sequence $R^n/n!$ is also bounded, it follows that there is an M such that

$$\left|\frac{f^{(n)}(s)}{n!} R^n\right| \leq M$$

for every s in $|x-t| \leq R$ and for $n = 1, 2, 3, \ldots$

Statements such as Corollary 6-21, which show that certain functions are analytic, are very useful in tracking down unknown functions. It often happens during the search for a formula that a unique analytic function is found which is compatible with the conditions of the problem. If it can be then shown that the function which is being sought is analytic, this solves the problem. Moreover, knowing that a function has a series representation often makes it possible to use a polynomial approximation to it, which facilitates the computations involved.

Exercises

1. Carry out the following instructions for each of the series of exercise 1(c) on page 102.

   (a) Find a series for the derivative of its sum function and test directly that its interval of convergence is the same as that of the original.

   (b) Find a series for an antiderivative of its sum function, and test directly that its interval of convergence is the same as that of the original.

2. (a) Find the MacLaurin series of f if $f(x) = 1/(1+5x)$.

   (b) Find the MacLaurin series for f' from the answer to part (a).

   (c) Find $f'(x)$ directly from $f(x)$, and find its MacLaurin series.

3. Show that if c is any number, then the sequence $1, c, c^2/2!, c^3/3!, \ldots$ is bounded. Use this to show that if $f' = cf$ for some interval $|x-t| < R$, then f is analytic. Find the MacLaurin series for f if $f(0) = 1$.

4. It is given that $f'' = f$ for some interval $(-R, R)$.

   (a) Show that f is analytic.

   (b) Find the MacLaurin series for f if $f(0) = 1, f'(0) = 0$.

   (c) Find the MacLaurin series for f if $f(0) = 0, f'(0) = 1$.

   (d) Find the MacLaurin series for f if $f(0) = a, f'(0) = b$.

   (e) Show that if $f(0) = 0$, $f'(0) = 0$, then $f(x) = 0$. for every x in $(-R, R)$.

5. It is given that $f'' = -cf$ for some interval $(t-R, t+R)$.

   (a) Show that f is analytic.

   (b) Find the Taylor series for f if $f(t) = 0, f'(t) = 1$.

   (c) Find the Taylor series for f if $f(t) = 1, f'(t) = 0$.

The Method of Undetermined Coefficients

Although there is no universally successful procedure for finding an unknown function, there is one which comes close enough to this unrealistic concept to warrant an examination. It is called the "method of undetermined coefficients." It consists of assuming that the problem has a power series solution and using the conditions of the problem to obtain equations for the unknown coefficients of this series. A conscientious investigator tests (a) whether the series so obtained is convergent, (b) whether its sum function meets the conditions of the problem, (c) how many terms must be used to attain a given standard of accuracy, and (d) whether there are other solutions to the problem which do not have series expansions. At the other end of the responsibility spectrum is the happy-go-lucky investigator. He uses the conditions of the problem to find the first few terms of a series, and uses these terms as an approximate formula for the unknown function. Each of these approaches, and many variants of them, can turn out to be the right one to use, depending, of course, on the problem itself. The method will be illustrated in a few representative situations.

ALGEBRAIC EQUATIONS $P(x, y) = 0$:   Let $P(x, y)$ be a polynomial in the variables x and y. For each value of x the equation $P(x, y) = 0$ is an algebraic equation for y which has, in general, many solutions. For instance if $P(x, y)$ is $x^2 + y^2 - 1$, then, for $x = 0$, the corresponding equation is $y^2 - 1 = 0$, and its solutions are 1 and -1. It is possible to find formulas which represent solutions of the equation $x^2 + y^2 - 1 = 0$ in terms of x, namely, $\sqrt{1 - x^2}$ and $-\sqrt{1 - x^2}$. For more complicated polynomials $P(x, y)$ it is not generally possible to solve the corresponding equation for y in terms of x by extracting roots. However, if for a certain value x_0 of x a solution y_0 of the equation $P(x_0, y) = 0$ is known, then it is generally possible to find a power series $y_0 + a_1(x - x_0) + a_1(x - x_0)^2 + \cdots$ which converges for every x in some interval $(x_0 - d, x_0 + d)$ to a solution of the equation $P(x, y) = 0$. The functions these equations define are called *algebraic functions* and have been extensively studied. It turns out that expansions for them can generally be found by the method of undetermined coefficients. Some of the relevant facts are set forth in the following theorem.

THEOREM 6-22:   Let $A_0(x)$, $A_1(x)$, $\ldots$, $A_n(x)$ be polynomials, let x_0 be a number, and let y_0 be a solution of the equation $A_0(x_0) + A_1(x_0)y + \cdots + A_n(x_0)y^n = 0$. Then, if y_0 is not a multiple root of this equation, there is a power series $y_0 + a_1(x - x_0) + a_2(x - x_0)^2 + \cdots$ which converges for every x in some interval $(x_0 - d, x_0 + d)$ to a solution of the equation

$$A_0(x) + A_1(x)y + \cdots + A_n(x)y^n = 0.$$

It is beyond the scope of this course to give a proof of this theorem and we do not attempt to do so.

To apply the theorem in any given case it is first necessary to find a pair (x_0, y_0) which satisfies the given equation. The next step is to substitute $y_0 + a_1(x - x_0) + a_2(x - x_0)^2 + \cdots$ for y in the equation and try to determine the unknowns $a_1, a_2, \ldots$ so that the series satisfies the equation. It turns out that the condition of the theorem about multiple roots works automatically—if the equations for the unknown coefficients are solvable, then the resulting series solves the problem, and if the equation for the unknown coefficients are not solvable, then the number y_0 is a multiple root.

Example: The equation $1 + x^2 y + y^5 = 0$ is satisfied by $(0, -1)$. We seek a power series solution $-1 + a_1 x + a_2 x^2 + \cdots$ of this equation. We substitute this power series for y in the given equation, obtaining

$$1 + x^2(-1 + a_1 x + a_2 x^2 + \cdots) + (-1 + a_1 x + a_2 x^2 + \cdots)^5 = 0.$$

Using

$$(-1 + a_1 x + a_2 x^2 + \cdots)^5 = -1 + 5a_1 x + (5a_2 - 10a_1^2)x^2 + \cdots,$$

this becomes

$$1 - 1 + 5a_1 x + (-1 - 10a_1^2 + 5a_2)x^2 + \cdots = 0.$$

This power series will satisfy the equation if and only if each of the coefficients $1 - 1$, $5a_1$, $-1 - 10a_1^2 + 5a_2$, ... is zero. These conditions determine the unknowns $a_1, a_2, \ldots$ uniquely. In particular, $a_1 = 0$, $a_2 = \frac{1}{5}$.

DIFFERENTIAL EQUATIONS: It sometimes happens that an unknown function is specified by an equation relating it to its derivatives. Such an equation is called a *differential equation*. The subject of differential equations has been studied extensively, and many different methods for trying to solve them are available. The following example shows how the method of undetermined coefficients can be used for this purpose.

Example: $y'' + 5y' + 6xy = 0$ is a differential equation for the unknown function y. To solve it we assume for y a series expansion $c_0 + c_1 x + c_2 x^2 + \cdots$ and try to determine the unknown coefficients $c_0, c_1, c_2, \ldots$ so that the given equation is satisfied. If this series is substituted for y, the series $c_1 + 2c_2 x + 3c_3 x^2 + \cdots$ for y', and $2c_2 + 6c_3 x + \cdots$ for y'' into the given equation we obtain

$$2c_2 + 5c_1 + (6c_3 + 10c_2 + 6c_0)x + (12c_4 + 15c_3 + 6c_1)x^2 + \cdots = 0.$$

The equation will be satisfied if the unknown coefficients satisfy $2c_2+5c_1 = 0$, $6c_3+10c_2+6c_0 = 0$, $12c_4+15c_3+6c_1 = 0$, ... We see that if we chose any values whatsoever for c_1 and c_0, these equations successively determine $c_2, c_3, c_4, \ldots$.

In this example, as in many other cases, the series obtained by the method of undetermined coefficients converges to a solution of the equation. The fact that the numbers c_0, c_1 can be chosen arbitrarily holds generally for differential equations in which the second derivative but no higher derivative of the unknown function appears. If derivatives up to order n appear in a differential equation, then generally it happens that the coefficients $c_0, c_1, \ldots, c_{n-1}$ can be chosen arbitrarily.

FUNCTIONAL EQUATIONS IN GENERAL: Algebraic equations and differential equations are two special types of functional equations. Any equation for an unknown function is a functional equation. The general theory of these equations is relatively undeveloped, but here, too, the method of undetermined coefficients often is useful.

Example: $f(x)+f(y) = f(x+y)$ is a functional equation. If we seek a series $a_0+a_1x+a_2x^2+ \cdots$ which converges to a solution of this equation, we obtain the condition

$$a_0+a_1x+a_2x^2+ \cdots +a_0+a_1y+a_2y^2+ \cdots$$
$$= a_0+a_1(x+y)+a_2(x+y)^2+ \cdots.$$

By equating coefficients of like terms we obtain the equations $2a_0 = a_0$, $a_1 = a_1$, $a_i = 0$ for $i = 2, 3, 4, \ldots$. Thus the only analytic function f which satisfies this functional equation is defined by $f(x) = a_1x$, where the number a_1 can be chosen arbitrarily.

Exercises

1. Find a_1 and a_2 if the power series $1+a_1x+a_2x^2+ \cdots$ satisfies
   (a) $y^2-2x-1 = 0$;   (b) $y^2-2xy-1 = 0$;   (c) $y^5-2xy-1 = 0$;
   (d) $y^3-xy^2+x-1 = 0$.

2. (Derivatives of algebraic functions). It is possible to find the derivative of a solution of an algebraic equation $P(x, y) = 0$ without actually solving the equation. Consider, for example, the equation

$$x^2y+xy^2-1 = 0,$$

and regard y not as an unknown but as the value at x of a solution of the equation. Then the left side is the zero function and its derivative is zero. We apply rules for finding derivatives of compound functions to obtain $2xy+x^2y'+y^2+2xyy'$ as the derivative of the left side. Equating this to zero and solving for y' yields

$$y' = (-y^2-2xy)/(x^2+2xy).$$

Apply this method to find y' if (a) $x^2+y^2-1 = 0$; (b) $xy-1 = 0$; (c) $1+x^3-2x^2y+y^2 = 0$; (d) $1+2xy+x^2y^2 = 0$. Check your answer in each case by solving for y and differentiating the resulting expression.

3. (Falling bodies). For a body falling under the influence of gravity, the altitude h of the body satisfies the differential equation (a) $h'' = -g$ if air resistance is neglected; (b) $h'' = -g-rh'$ if air resistance is assumed to be proportional to the speed; (c) $h'' = -g+rh'^2$ if air resistance is assumed to be proportional to the square of the speed. Find the first four terms of a series solution for each of these differential equations subject to the conditions $h(0) = h_0$, $h'(0) = v_0$. (The number g is approximately 32, and the number r depends on the shape of the body and other physical circumstances.)

4. Find all power series $P(x)$ if (a) $P(x)^2 = P(x)$; (b) $P(x)^2 = xP(x)$; (c) $P(ax)+P(bx) = P((a+b)x)$; (d) $P(ax)P(bx) = P((a+b)x)$.

CHAPTER 7

Series Expansions
of the
Elementary Functions

This chapter has two aims. One is to give a development of the elementary functions which is logically self-sufficient. Much of what the high schools present on this subject is valuable, but it is not, nor does it pretend to be, a rigorous account, such as the one we seek here. We shall not ignore the high school background of this topic, but we shall not build on it logically. The second aim of the chapter is to show a certain method in action. The method consists in finding and studying unknown functions by finding power series representations for them. We shall only deal with the elementary functions, but the method can be applied to a far wider class of functions, and the chapter should dispose the student to do so.

The Exponential Functions

We learn early in our mathematical careers that exponents are convenient abbreviations for repeated multiplications; for instance, $2 \cdot 2 \cdot 2 \cdot 2 = 2^4$, $6 \cdot 6 \cdot 6 = 6^3$, etc. We also learn a rule governing the behavior of exponents to the effect that $a^n \cdot a^m = a^{n+m}$. Later we learn to use more complicated exponents, negative integers and fractions. We learn, for instance, that if a is any positive real number and n is any positive integer, then there is one and only one real number x for which $x^n = a$. We learn to call this number by two names, $a^{1/n}$ and $\sqrt[n]{a}$. We learn to use $a^{m/n}$ to designate $(a^{1/n})^m$, where n is any positive integer and m is any integer whatsoever. We learn that the rule $a^p \cdot a^q = a^{p+q}$ also applies to this more general kind of exponent.

We now seek an interpretation of a^x which is valid not only for fractions but for every real number x. We require also that our interpretation shall be such that $a^x \cdot a^y = a^{x+y}$. For instance, we seek meanings for $3^{\sqrt{10}}$ and 3^π such that $3^{\sqrt{10}} \cdot 3^\pi = 3^{\sqrt{10}+\pi}$. Our procedure is to seek a function f, defined for every real value of x, for which $f(x) f(y) = f(x+y)$. We require that this function should generalize our notion of exponent (a) by agreeing with it for rational values of x and (b) by not giving strange results for irrational values of x. Toward meeting this last requirement we require that f be continuous. We also require that at least for one value of x, $f(x) \neq 0$. It follows from $f(x) = f(x+0) = f(x)$ that $f(0) = 1$. We assume also that f is differentiable at $x = 0$. This implies that there is a number c such that $f(x) = f(x) - cx$ has order one at 0.

First we show that f is differentiable at every t. By substituting 1 for $f(0)$ and $x - t$ for x in our last expression, we infer that $f(x-t) - 1 - c(x-t)$ has order one at t. Therefore, the product $f(t)(f(x-t) - 1 - c(x-t))$ has order one at t. Using the fact that $f(t) f(x-t) = f(t + (x-t)) = f(x)$, we see that $f(x) - f(t) - cf(t)(x-t)$ has order one at t. It follows that f is differentiable at t and that its derivative at t is $cf(t)$. We see that, for every x, $f'(x) = cf(x)$, where c is $f'(0)$. We see from this relation that f' is also differentiable and $f'' = c^2 f$; that also $f''' = c^3 f$, and in general, $f^{(n)} = c^n f$, $n = 1, 2, \ldots$.

Thus our search for a generalization of the exponents of algebra leads us to seek, for each number c, a function f for which $f(0) = 1, f'(0) = c$, $f''(0) = c^2, \ldots, f^n(0) = c^n, \ldots$. If there were such a function, its series expansion at 0 would be

$$1 + cx + \frac{c^2 x^2}{2!} + \cdots + \frac{c^n x^n}{n!} + \cdots.$$

It was shown in Example (b), page 100, that for each c, this series converges for every value of x. We call the functions defined by these series *exponential functions*. The function associated with the value $c = 1$ is especially important. Its value at x is often denoted by $\exp (x)$. Note that the functions associated with values of c other than 1 are simply $\exp (cx)$. The value of $\exp (x)$ at $x = 1$, namely, $1 + 1 + 1/2! + 1/3! + \cdots$ is denoted by e. This number has no finite decimal representation, and is, in fact, irrational. Its approximate value is 2.7182. This number e, like the number π, presents itself in many mathematical investigations.

We were led to the function exp (x) in our search for a function which had the exponent property $a^x \cdot a^y = a^{x+y}$. The next theorem shows that exp (x) does in fact have this property.

THEOREM 7-1: exp $(x+t) =$ exp (x) exp (t) for every t and every x.

Proof: The n-th derivative of exp $(x+t)$ at $x = 0$ is exp (t), for $n = 1, 2, 3, \ldots$. Therefore, the MacLaurin series for exp $(x+t)$ is exp $(t) +$ exp $(t)x + \cdots +$ exp $(t)(x/n!) + \cdots$, which converges to exp (t) exp (x) for every x.

COROLLARY 7-2: exp $(-x) = 1/$exp (x).

Proof: exp (x) exp $(-x) =$ exp $(x-x) =$ exp $(0) = 1$.

COROLLARY 7-3: If n is any positive integer, then $(\exp(x))^n =$ exp (nx).

COROLLARY 7-4: If n is any positive integer, then exp $(-nx) = 1/(\exp(x))^n$.

The shape of the graph of the function exp is indicated by the following theorem.

THEOREM 7-5:

(1)   If $t > 0$, then exp $(t) > 1$;

(2)   If $b > 1$, there is one and only one t such that $t > 0$ and exp $(t) = b$;

(3)   If $t < 0$, then $0 <$ exp $(t) < 1$;

(4)   If $0 < b < 1$, there is one and only one t such that $t < 0$ and exp $(t) = b$.

Proof: It is clear from the series expansion for exp (x) that if $x > 0$, then exp $(x) > 1+x$. This proves (1). If $b > 1$, then exp $(b) > 1+b$. Since exp $(0) = 1$ and since exp is continuous, there is a t between 0 and b for which exp $(t) = b$. Since exp is its own derivative, (1) implies that it is an increasing function for positive x. This shows that there cannot be two different positive values of t for which exp $(t) = b$. This proves (2). Items (3) and (4) follow now from the fact that exp $(-x) = 1/$exp (x).

COROLLARY 7-6: exp (x) is an increasing function which traces out the set of positive real numbers as x traces out the set of all real numbers.

Sometimes exp (x) is denoted by e^x. Since e^x has a meaning for rational values of x (for instance, e^2 means $e \cdot e$), it is worthwhile to show that, for these values of x, the two interpretations of e^x give the same value. For $x = 1$ this is a restatement of the definition. For any other rational value of x this follows readily from Theorem 7-1 and its corollaries. We can also give a meaning to b^t for every real number t and every positive number b.

DEFINITION: If $b > 0$, then b^t means exp (at), where a is the number for which exp $(a) = b$.

THEOREM 7-7: If $b > 0$, then

(1) $b^{p+q} = b^p \cdot b^q$;

(2) $b^{pr} = (b^p)^r$.

Proof: Let $b = \exp(a)$. Since $b^p = \exp(ap)$ and $b^q = \exp(aq)$, then $b^p \cdot b^q = \exp(ap+aq) = \exp(a(p+q)) = b^{p+q}$. Finally, invoking our last definition repeatedly, we have

$$(b^p)^r = (\exp(ap))^r = \exp(apr) = b^{pr}.$$

Exercises

1. Find the Taylor series for e^x with center   (a) 1;   (b) -1;   (c) t.

2. Find the Taylor series for a^x with center   (a) 0;   (b) 1;   (c) -1);   (d) t.

3. Say what is meant by each of the following, in terms of the exponential function.   (a) $e^{\sqrt{2}}$;   (b) $(\sqrt{3})^{\sqrt{2}}$;   (c) $e^{\sqrt{2}}$;   (d) $(\sqrt{2})^e$;   (e) $a^{\sqrt{2}}$;   (f) a^b.

4. Find the derivative of f if $f(x)$ is   (a) e^{2x};   (b) e^{x^2};   (c) e^{-x^2};   (d) $e^{\sqrt{x}}$;   (e) $e^{\sqrt{x^2-2x}}$.

5. Find the derivative of f if $f(x)$ is   (a) 10^x;   (b) 10^{2x};   (c) 10^{x^2};   (d) $10^{\sqrt{x}}$;   (e) $10^{(4^x)}$.

6. Show that if f is a function for which $f' = 5f$, then this is a number c such that $f(x) = ce^{5x}$. Show that there is only one function f for which $f' = 5f$ and $f(0) = 27$. Find it.

7. Find a power series representation for f if $f''(x) = 3f'(x) - 2f(x)$ and $f(0) = 1, f'(0) = 1$.

8. In a room at temperature $70°$ at $t = 0$, a cup of coffee has temperature $150°$, and at $t = 1$ it has temperature $148°$. What is a reasonable estimate of its temperature at $t = 2$? for any t? [Hint: Assume the rate of change of temperature is proportional to the temperature difference between the coffee and the room. Then if $f(t)$ is a formula for the temperature at time t, there is some number c such that $f'(t) = c(f(t) - 70)$.]

9. The rate of growth of a certain colony of bacteria is proportional to the size of the colony. Find a formula $S(t)$ for the size of the colony in terms of the time t, if $S(0) = 100$, $S(20) = 50$.

10. The rate of decay of a certain radioactive substance is proportional to the amount remaining. Find a formula $A(t)$ for the amount A in terms of the time t if $A(0) = 500$, $A(20) = 100$.

11. Let $ax^2 + bx + c = 0$ be a quadratic equation with real roots r and s. Show that $af''(x) + bf'(x) + cf(x) = 0$ is satisfied if (a) $f = e^{rx}$; (b) $f = e^{sx}$; (c) $f = pe^{rx} + qe^{sx}$ (where p and q are numbers). Discuss the possibility of representing a function f by an expression $pe^{rx} + qe^{sx}$ if it is given that $af''(x) + bf'(x) + cf(x) = 0$.

12. Prove the following:
    (a) if $x \geq 0$, then $e^x > x^n/n!$, for $n = 1, 2, \ldots$;
    (b) if $x \geq 0$ and if $a > 0$, then there is an x_0 such that if $x > x_0$, then $e^{ax} > x^n/n!$, for $n = 1, 2, \ldots$;
    (c) if $Q(x)$ is any monomial px^n and if $a > 0$, then there is an x_0 such that if $x > x_0$, then $e^{ax} > Q(x)$;
    (d) if $Q(x)$ is any polynomial and if $a > 0$, then there is an x_0 such that if $x > x_0$, then $e^{ax} > Q(x)$.

Logarithms; The Binomial Theorem

The exponential function has an inverse, namely, the logarithm, which is useful in its own right. Many of us first meet logarithms as an aid to calculation. The modern computer has greatly reduced the importance of logarithms for this purpose, but there remain many theoretical situations in which logarithms are important.

It is clear from Theorem 7-5 that the exponential functions have inverses. These inverses are the logarithm functions.

DEFINITIONS: If b is a positive number, the *base b logarithm* is the inverse of the function whose value at x is b^x. The base e logarithm is called the *natural* logarithm.

Notation: We denote the base b logarithm by $\log_b$, and denote the natural logarithm sometimes by $\log_e$, sometimes by log and sometimes by ln.

Examples:
(a)   Since $10^2 = 100$, $\log_{10} 100 = 2$;
(b) $\log e^2 = 3$;
(c) $\ln e^t = t = e^{\ln t}$.

Referring to Corollary 7-6, we see that as x traces out the set of positive real numbers, $\log_b x$ traces out the set of real numbers. Clearly, $\log_b b^t = t = b^{\log_b t}$, for every positive b and every t. From this it follows readily that $\log_b (uv) = \log_b u + \log_b v$ and $\log_b (u^t) = t \log_b u$. If we combine the facts that b^p means $(e^a)^p$, where $e^a = b$, with the definition of logarithms, we see that $\log_e x = \log_e b \log_b x$. This expresses $\log_b x$ in terms of natural logarithms. It also shows that $\log_e b \cdot \log_b e = \log_e^e = 1$. Since exp is differentiable and has a nonzero derivative at every x, it follows from Theorem 4-13 that log is differentiable at every x.

THEOREM 7-8: $\log' (x) = 1/x$ for every positive x.

Proof: According to Theorem 4-13, we have $\log' (x) = 1/\exp' (\log x)$. Since $\exp' = \exp$, and since $\exp (\log x) = x$, our result follows.

COROLLARY 7-9:   If n is any real number, then at every positive x the derivative of x^n is nx^{n-1}.

Proof: $x^n = \exp (n \log x)$, $(x^n)' = \exp (n \log x) \cdot (n/x) = x^n \cdot (n/x) = nx^{n-1}$.

COROLLARY 7-10:   The n-th derivative of log at x is $(-1)(-2) \cdots (-n+1)x^{-n}$.

COROLLARY 7-11:   The Taylor expansion of log at t is

$$\log t + \frac{1}{t}(x-t) - \frac{1}{2t^2}(x-t)^2 - \cdots + \frac{(-1)^{n+1}}{nt^n}(x-t)^n + \cdots$$

Note: According to Theorem 6-20, this series converges to $\log x$ for $0 < x < 2t$.

COROLLARY 7-12:   The Taylor expansion of log at 1 is

$$(x-1) - \frac{1}{2}(x-1)^2 + \frac{1}{3}(x-1)^3 + \cdots + \frac{(-1)^{n-1}}{n}(x-1)^n + \cdots$$

Note: This series converges to $\log x$ for $0 < x < 2$.

COROLLARY 7-13:   For $|x| < 1$,

$$\log(1+x) = S\left(x - \frac{x^2}{2} + \frac{x^3}{3} + \cdots + \frac{(-1)^{n+1}}{n}x^n + \cdots\right).$$

Instead of restricting n to positive integral values, by using logarithms and exponentials we can expand $(1+x)^n$ into a series for every real number n. To see this, first note that $(1+x)^n$ means $\exp(n \log(1+x))$. Since the latter is the compositive of two functions with Taylor expansions, the former will have for its Taylor expansion the composite of the two series.

THEOREM 7-14   (Binomial Theorem):   If $|x| < 1$ and if n is any real number, then

$$1 + \frac{n}{1}x + \frac{n(n-1)}{1 \cdot 2}x^2 + \cdots + \frac{n(n-1) \cdots (n-r+1)}{r!}x^r + \cdots$$

converges to $(1+x)^n$.

Proof: According to Corollary 7-9, the n-th derivative of $(1+x)^n$ at x is $n(n-1) \ldots (n-m+1)(1+x)^{n-m}$. The values of $(1+x)^n$ and its derivatives at 0 are $1, n, n(n-1), \ldots, n(n-1) \ldots (n-m+1), \ldots$. We infer that the series proposed for $(1+x)^n$ is actually its Taylor series at $x = 0$. That it converges for $|x| < 1$ to $(1+x)^n$ follows from Theorem 6-20.

The formula $\log'(x) = 1/x$ enables us to find new antiderivatives.

Examples:

(a) An antiderivative of $1/(x+a)$ for every a is $\log (x+a)$;

(b) An antiderivative of $1/(ax+b)$ for every b and every nonzero a is $(1/a) \log (ax+b)$, since the derivative of the latter is $1/a \cdot 1/(ax+b) \cdot a$.

(c) An antiderivative of $1/(1-x^2)$ is $(1/2) \log ((1+x)/(1-x))$. To see this, note that

$$\frac{1}{1-x^2} = \frac{1}{2}\left(\frac{1}{1+x} + \frac{1}{1-x}\right)$$

and then use Examples (a) and (b) to see that an antiderivative is $\frac{1}{2}(\log (1+x) - \log (1-x))$.

Exercises

1. Find the derivative of the function defined by each:

(a) $\log (x^2)$ (d) $\log (2^x)$ (g) $\log (a^x)$

(b) $(\log x)^2$ (e) $\log (3+4x-5x^2)$ (h) $\log (\log x)$

(c) $\log (2x)$ (f) $\log (e^x)$ (i) $\log_b (x)$

(j) $\log_b f(x)$, where f is any differentiable function having only positive values.

2. Show that the area under the hyperbola $xy=1$ from 1 to t is $\log t$.

3. Show that

$$x + \frac{x^3}{3} + \frac{x^5}{5} + \cdots + \frac{x^{2n+1}}{2n+1} + \cdots$$

converges to $\dfrac{1}{2} \log \left(\dfrac{1+x}{1-x}\right)$ for $|x| < 1$.

4. Find the derivative of f if $f(x)$ is

(a) x^x.   [Hint: $x^x = e^{x \log x}$.]

(b) x^{x^2}.   [Hint: $x^{x^2} = e^{2x \log x}$.]

(c) $x^{(2^x)}$.   [Hint: $x^{(2^x)} = e^{2^x \log 2^x}$.]

(d) $P(x)^{q(x)}$.   [Hint: $P(x)^{q(x)} = e^{q(x) \log P(x)}$.]

5. Show that if r and s are unequal numbers, then there are numbers a and b such that

$$\frac{px+q}{(x-r)(x-s)} = \frac{a}{x-r} + \frac{b}{x-s}.$$

Use this result to find antiderivatives of

(a) $\dfrac{1}{x^2-1}$; (b) $\dfrac{x}{x^2-1}$; (c) $\dfrac{3x+4}{x^2-3x+2}$; (d) $\dfrac{3x^3+4x+5}{x^2-1}$.

[Hint: Express $3x^3+4x+5$ as $A(x)(x^2-1)+B(x)$ and rewrite the quotient as $A(x)+B(x)/(x^2-1)$.]

6. Show that there are numbers a and b such that

$$\frac{px+q}{(x-r)^2}=\frac{a}{(x-r)^2}+\frac{b}{x-r}.$$

Use this result to find antiderivatives of

(a) $\dfrac{3x}{(x+1)^2}$; (b) $\dfrac{3x+4}{(x+1)^2}$; (c) $\dfrac{3x^2+4x+5}{(x+1)^2}$.

7. (a) Find $\log \frac{3}{2}$ approximately, using the MacLaurin series for $\log (1+x)$.

  (b) Find $\log 9$ approximately, using the MacLaurin series for $\log ((1+x)/(1-x))$.

8. What is the MacLaurin series for $(a+bx)^n$, if $b \neq 0$? [Hint: $a+bx = a(1+(b/a)x)$.]

9. What is the MacLaurin series for $1/\sqrt{1-x^2}$? What is the MacLaurin series of an antiderivative of the function defined by this expression?

10. Same as Exercise 9 for $1/(1+x^2)$.

11. Show that

  (a) log is a strictly increasing function;

  (b) as x traces out the positive real numbers, $\log x$ traces out the real numbers.

12. Show that

  (a) x^a is strictly increasing if $a > 0$;

  (b) x^a traces out the positive real numbers as x traces out the positive real numbers $(a > 0)$;

  (c) x^a is strictly decreasing if $a < 0$;

  (d) x^a traces out the positive real numbers as x traces out the positive real numbers $(a < 0)$;

  (e) if $a > b$, then for every nonzero p and q there is an x_0 such that if $x > x_0$, then $|px^a| > |qx^b|$ [hint: try to arrive at $x^{a-b} > |q/p|$];

  (f) if $a > 0$ and if p and q are any numbers, then there is an x_0 such that if $x > x_0$, then $e^{ax} > px^q$ (compare with Exercise 12(c) in the preceding section, where q was an integer);

(g) if $a > 0$ and if $p > 0$, then there is an x_0 such that if $x > x_0$, then
log $x < px^a$;

(h) if $x > 1$, then log log $x < $ log x.

Trigonometric Functions

The student first meets the sine, cosine, tangent and the other trigonometric functions in high school, as aids in solving problems about triangles. The functions themselves, originally introduced for solving problems in geometry, have long since acquired many other roles, both in pure and applied mathematics. We are going to re-examine these functions in terms of power series. No prior knowledge of geometry or trigonometry will be used in our formal development. Much of the development of these subjects in high school mathematics is frankly incomplete, and it is often stated there that the student should expect a mathematically correct treatment only when he studies calculus. It would be illogical to propose as a mathematically correct treatment a discussion which accepted as sound this high school approach and merely continued it. Our attitude is that the high school approach first defines functions and then makes it plausible that these functions have certain perfectly definite properties. It will be shown that there are indeed functions with these properties and that these functions are unique. This will justify the identification of the functions introduced here with those discussed in high school.

There are at least two topics of elementary geometry and trigono-metry which resist rigorous yet elementary presentation, the addition of angles and the measurement of angles. Addition of angles requires that a duplicate of a given angle be constructed which has a prescribed side. The difficulty here, in general, is that two duplicates are available, that only one is wanted, and that the orientation concept needed to select the right one is rarely available in elementary geometry. Measure-ment of angles also requires this orientation concept, and probably some mastery of the concept of arc length as well, also a concept rarely available in elementary geometry.

We seek two functions, s and c (inspired by sine and cosine), which are defined for every real number and which have the following proper-ties (inspired by familiar formulas of trigonometry):

(1) $s(x+y) = s(x)c(y) + c(x)s(y)$;

(2) $c(x+y) = c(x)c(y) - s(x)s(y)$.

We assume further that c and s are differentiable, that $c'(0) = 0$ and that $s'(0) \neq 0$. In what follows, c and s denote any functions which meet these conditions, and a is $s'(0)$.

LEMMA 7-15: $c(0) = 1$, $s(0) = 0$.

Proof: Substitute 0 for y in (1) and (2), obtaining

$$s(x) = s(x)c(0) + c(x)s(0)$$
$$c(x) = c(x)c(0) - s(x)s(0).$$

Direct substitution shows that $c(0) = 1$, $s(0) = 0$ is a solution of this system. Because $s'(0) \neq 0$, we cannot have $s(x) = 0$ for every x. Because $s(x)^2 + c(x)^2 \neq 0$, this system of equations for $c(0)$ and $s(0)$ has a unique solution.

LEMMA 7-16: $s' = ac$, $c' = -as$.

Proof: Use the chain rule and the rule for differentiating sums and differences to obtain from (1) and (2)

$$s'(x+y) = s'(x)c(y) + c'(x)s(y)$$
$$c'(x+y) = c'(x)c(y) - s'(x)s(y)$$

and then replace x by 0.

COROLLARY 7-17: $s^{(2n)} = (-1)^n a^{2n}s$,
$$s^{(2n+1)} = (-1)^n a^{2n+1}x,$$
$$c^{(2n)} = (-1)^n a^{2n}c,$$
$$c^{(2n+1)} = (-1)^{n+1} a^{2n+1}c.$$

COROLLARY 7-18: The series

$$ax - \frac{(ax)^3}{3!} + \cdots + \frac{(-1)^{i+1}(-ax)^{2i+1}}{(2i+1)!} + \cdots$$

is the MacLaurin series for s. It converges for every x. The series

$$1 - \frac{(ax)^2}{2!} + \cdots + \frac{(-1)^i(ax)^{2i}}{(2i)!} + \cdots$$

is the MacLaurin series for c. It converges for every x.

For each nonzero a we have found that there is at most one pair of functions s and c which meets the stated conditions. The pair corresponding to the value $a = 1$ is clearly the primary one, since, if we denote the corresponding functions by s_1 and c_1, the values at x of the functions corresponding to a are $s_1(ax)$ and $c_1(ax)$.

It is not surprising that an arbitrary constant a should turn up in our search for trigonometric functions. It reflects the need for choosing a unit angle. For instance, if the sin was considered to be a function of angles, then its value at a right angle would be 1, without ambiguity. However, the switch to angle measure introduces different functions, one for each unit angle, which are associated with this function of angles. One of them, for instance, has the value 1 at 90 (the degree is the unit angle) and another has the value 1 at $\pi/2$ (the radian is the unit angle). We shall see that the decision to use $a = 1$, which was made to simplify the formulas, has the effect of selecting the radian as the unit angle.

DEFINITIONS: sin is the function whose value at x is

$$S\left(x - \frac{x^3}{3!} + \cdots + \frac{(-1)^{n+1}x^{2n+1}}{(2n+1)!} + \cdots\right);$$

cos is the function whose value at x is

$$S\left(1 - \frac{x^2}{2!} + \cdots + \frac{(-1)^n x^{2n}}{(2n)!} + \cdots\right).$$

Note: Although formulas (1) and (2) were used in our search for trigonometric functions, we have not proved that the functions sin and cos obey them. It is left as an exercise for the reader to verify directly from the series that they do. It is plain from the series that $\sin(0) = 0$, $\sin'(0) = 1$, $\cos(0) = 1$, $\cos'(0) = 0$.

LEMMA 7-19: $\sin(-x) = -\sin x$, $\cos(-x) = \cos x$, $\sin^2 x + \cos^2 x = 1$.

Proof: The first two follow from an examination of the series for sin and cos; the third follows from these results, after substituting $-x$ for y in formula (2).

It will now be shown that the functions sin and cos are periodic, with period 2π, i.e., that $\sin(x+2\pi) = \sin x$, $\cos(x+2\pi) = \cos x$. In this relation π is the well-known real number with approximate value 3.1416, which denotes the ratio of half the circumference of a circle to the length of its radius. In spite of the familiarity of π, in our formal development we maintain our policy of nondependence on high school geometry. Thus when we encounter the number called "π," we shall have no official information about its role in geometry. We shall first deduce that there is a smallest positive real number t such that $\cos t = 0$. This number is called "$\pi/2$." In a later section it will be shown that the circumference of a circle is 2π and that the arc length subtended by a central angle of measure 1 in a circle of radius π is r. This will identify the π of the present study with the π of geometry, and it will connect the trigonometric functions corresponding to $a = 1$ with the choice of the radian as the unit angle.

LEMMA 7-20: $\cos 2 < 0$.

Proof: $\cos 2$ is the sum of the alternating series
$$1 - (2^2/2!) + (2^4/4!) + \cdots.$$
Therefore,
$$\left| \cos 2 - \left(1 - \frac{2^2}{2!} \right) \right| < \frac{2^4}{4!}.$$
But $1 - (2^2/2!) = -1$, and $2^2/4! = 2/3$, so our result follows.

COROLLARY 7-21:   There is a number c between 0 and 2 for which $\cos c = 0$.

Proof: $\cos$ is continuous, $\cos 0 > 0$, $\cos 2 < 0$.

COROLLARY 7-22:   There is a positive number d, for which $\cos d = 0$, which is smaller than any other positive solution of the equation $\cos x = 0$.

Proof: Apply Lemma 6-8.

DEFINITION: The smallest positive solution of $\cos x = 0$ is called $\pi/2$.

LEMMA 7-23:   The values of sin and cos obey the following.

x	$\sin x$	$\cos x$
(1) Increases from 0 to $\pi/2$	Increases from 0 to 1	Decreases from 1 to 0
(2) Increases from $\pi/2$ to π	Decreases from 1 to 0	Decreases from 0 to -1
(3) Increases from π to $3\pi/2$	Decreases from 0 to -1	Increases from -1 to 0
(4) Increases from $3\pi/2$ to 2π	Increases from -1 to 0	Increases from 0 to 1

Proof:

(1) We infer from $\sin^2 \pi/2 + \cos^2 \pi/2 = 1$ and $\cos \pi/2 = 0$ that $\sin \pi/2 = \pm 1$. Since $\sin' = \cos$ and $\cos x > 0$ for $0 \le x < \pi/2$, we infer that sin is increasing on that interval. Since $\sin 0 = 0$, we infer that $\sin \pi/2 > 0$, whence $\sin \pi/2 = 1$. Because $\cos' = -\sin$, and because $\sin x > 0$ if $0 < x \le \pi/2$, it can be seen that $\cos x$ is decreasing for these values. It is already known that $\cos 0 = 1$ and $\cos \pi/2 = 0$.

(2) We have $\sin (\pi/2 + x) = \sin \pi/2 \cos x + \cos \pi/2 \sin x = \cos x$. This identifies the behavior of $\sin x$ on $\pi/2 \le x \le \pi$ with that of $\cos x$ on $0 \le x \le \pi/2$. We have $\cos (\pi/2 + x) = \cos \pi/2 \cos x - \sin \pi/2 \sin x = -\sin x$. As x increases from 0 to $\pi/2$, $\sin x$ increases from 0 to 1, $-\sin x$ decreases from 0 to -1, $x + \pi/2$ increases from $\pi/2$ to π, $\cos (x + \pi/2)$ decreases from 0 to -1.

(3) and (4). We have $\sin (x + \pi) = \sin x \cos \pi + \cos x \sin \pi = -\sin x$ and $\cos (x + \pi) = \cos x \cos \pi - \sin x \sin \pi = -\cos \pi$. These relations express the behavior of $\sin x$ and $\cos x$ for $\pi \le x \le 2\pi$ in terms of their behavior for $0 \le x \le \pi$ and verify our assertions.

COROLLARY 7-24: $\sin (-2\pi) = 0$, $\cos (-2\pi) = 1$.

COROLLARY 7-25: $\sin (2n\pi) = 0$,
$\cos (2n\pi) = 1, n = 0, \pm 1, \pm 2, \ldots$.

THEOREM 7-26: For every real x and for every integer n we have $\sin (x + 2n\pi) = \sin x$, $\cos (x + 2n\pi) = \cos x$. If for some numbers a and b we have $\sin a = \sin b$, $\cos a = \cos b$, then there is an integer n such that $b = a + 2n\pi$.

Proof: We have

$$\sin (x + 2n\pi) = \sin x \cos 2n\pi + \cos x \sin 2n\pi$$

$$= (\sin x) \cdot 1 + (\cos x) \cdot 0 = \sin x,$$

$$\cos (x = 2n\pi) = \cos x \cos 2n\pi - \sin x \sin 2n\pi = \cos x.$$

If $\sin a = \sin b$ and $\cos a = \cos b$, then

$$\cos (a - b) = \cos a \cos b + \sin a \sin b$$
$$= \cos^2 a + \sin^2 a$$
$$= 1.$$

The number $a - b$ is therefore an integral multiple of 2π.

Exercises

1. Prove directly from the series that the functions defined by the Taylor series which represent sin and cos have properties (1) and (2) (page 123).

2. Expand sin and cos in powers of $x-t$.

3. Derive the formulas
   (a) $\sin 2x = 2 \sin x \cos x$
   (b) $\cos 2x = \cos^2 x - \sin^2 x = 2 \cos^2 x - 1 = 1 - 2 \sin^2 x$
   (c) $\cos (x/2) = \pm \dfrac{\sqrt{1 \cos x}}{2}$
   (d) $\sin (x/2) = \pm \dfrac{\sqrt{1 - \cos x}}{2}$
   (e) $\sin x = \cos (\pi/2 - x)$
   (f) $\cos x = \sin (\pi/2 - x)$

4. Find the exact values of
   (a) $\sin \pi/4$ (d) $\cos \pi/3$
   (b) $\cos \pi/4$ (e) $\sin \pi/6$
   (c) $\sin \pi/3$ (f) $\cos \pi/6$

5. (a) Show that there is no x for which $0 < x < \pi$ such that $\sin x = 0$;
   (b) Do the same for $\pi < x < 2\pi$.

6. Using Exercise 5, show that the only numbers c for which $\sin (x+c) = \sin x$ for every x are $0, \pm 2\pi, \pm 4\pi, \ldots$.

7. Find $f'(x)$ if $f(x)$ is
   (a) $\sin 2x$ (d) $\cos (x/2)$ (h) $\cos^2 x$
   (b) $\cos 2x$ (e) $\sin (3x+4)$ (i) $\sin (x^2)$
   (c) $\sin (x/2)$ (f) $\cos (ax+b)$ (j) $\cos (x^2)$
                               (g) $\sin^2 x$ (k) $\log (\sin x)$

8. Define $\tan x$ as $\sin x/\cos x$. Find the derivative of tan. Find the first four terms of the MacLaurin series for tan.

9. Do the same as in Exercise 8 for
   (a) $\cot x = \cos x/\sin x$
   (b) $\sec x = 1/\cos x$

10. *Simple harmonic motion.* A particle moves on a line so that its acceleration at time t is proportional to its distance $f(t)$ from a given point. Show that

(a) for some number c, $f''(t) = cf(t)$ for every time t;

(b) if c is negative, $\sin(\sqrt{-c}\,t)$ satisfies the condition of the problem.

(c) the same applies to $\cos(\sqrt{-c}\,t)$;

(d) the same applies to $A \sin(\sqrt{-c}\,t+B)$ where A and B are any numbers;

(e) the same applies to $A \cos(\sqrt{-c}\,t+B)$ where A and B are any numbers;

(f) Relate the number A of (d) and (e) to the maximum distance the particle gets from the given point.

(g) Show that if the particle's position and velocity are prescribed for some time t_0, its position at every time t is thereby determined.

(h) Show that any particle moving so as to satisfy the conditions of the problem (with $c < 0$) has a position formula $A \sin(\sqrt{-c}\,t+B)$, where A and B are some numbers.

(i) Show that the motion of the particle is periodic if $c < 0$.

(j) Show that, if $c > 0$, the position of the particle is given by the formula $Ae^{\sqrt{c}t}+Be^{-\sqrt{c}t}$, where A and B are some numbers.

(k) Show that, if $c < 0$, the distance of the particle from the fixed point is unbounded.

11. Let $i = \sqrt{-1}$. Show from the series for the functions involved that

(a) $e^{ix} = \cos x + i \sin x$

(c) $\cos x = \dfrac{e^{ix}+e^{-ix}}{2}$

(b) $\sin x = \dfrac{e^{ix}-e^{-ix}}{2i}$

(d) $e^{i\pi} = -1$

Inverse Trigonometric Functions

The inverse trigonometric functions often turn up in applications of mathematics to situations having no obvious connection with trigonometry. Generally it is their derivatives which appear first, and these functions come into the discussion as antiderivatives. We compute the derivatives of the three principal inverse trigonometric functions now.

LEMMA 7-27: sin is strictly increasing on $-\pi/2 < x < \pi/2$, cos is strictly decreasing on $0 < x < \pi$, and tan is strictly increasing on $-\pi/2 < x < \pi/2$.

Proof: The assertions about sin and cos have already been established. Since tan $=$ sin/cos, we have

$$\tan' = \frac{\cos \sin' - \sin \cos}{\cos^2}$$

$$= \frac{\cos^2 + \sin^2}{\cos^2}$$

$$= \frac{1}{\cos^2}.$$

Therefore $\tan'(x)$ is positive for $-\pi/2 < x < \pi/2$ and tan is strictly increasing there.

COROLLARY 7-28: $\tan' = 1/\cos^2$.

THEOREM 7-29:

(a)   The function whose value is $\sin x$, for $-\pi/2 < x < \pi/2$ has an inverse $\sin^{-1}$ and $(\sin^{-1})'(x) = 1/\sqrt{1-x^2}$.

(b)   The function whose value is $\cos x$ for $0 < x < \pi/2$ has an inverse $\cos^{-1}$, and $(\cos^{-1})'(x) = -1/\sqrt{1-x^2}$.

(c)   The function whose value is $\tan x$ for $-\pi/2 < x < \pi/2$ has an inverse $\tan^{-1}$, and $(\tan^{-1})'(x) = 1/(1+x^2)$.

Proof: That these functions have inverses follows from Lemma 7-27. To show that these inverses have the indicated derivatives we use the formula $(f^{-1})'(x) = 1/f'(f^{-1}(x))$. Since $\sin' = \cos$, we infer that $(\sin^{-1})'(x) = 1/\cos(\sin^{-1} x)$. Because $\cos^2 u = 1 - \sin^2 u$, for every u, we infer that the denominator of this expression is either $-\sqrt{1-x^2}$ or $-\sqrt{1-x^2}$. Since our function is the inverse of an increasing function, and therefore itself increasing, the positive square root must be chosen. Since $\cos' = -\sin$, we infer that $(\cos^{-1})'(x) = -1/\sin(\cos^{-1} x)$. The denominator of this expression is either $+\sqrt{1-x^2}$ or $-\sqrt{1-x^2}$. Since our function is the inverse of a decreasing function, $-1\sqrt{1-x^2}$ is the correct formula. Since $\tan' = 1/\cos^2$, we infer that $(\tan^{-1})'(x) = \cos^2(\tan^{-1} x)$. Because

$$\tan^2 u = \frac{\sin^2 u}{\cos^2 u} = \frac{1 - \cos^2 u}{\cos^2 u},$$

we have

$$\cos^2 u = \frac{1}{1+\tan^2 u}, \quad \text{so} \quad \cos^2(\tan^{-1} x) = \frac{1}{1+x^2}.$$

These new formulas, together with those already established, make it possible to verify all the entries in the following table of antiderivatives involving ax^2+bx+c, where $a \neq 0$ and $c \neq 0$.

$f'(x)$	$f(x)$	
$\dfrac{1}{ax^2+bx+c}$	$\dfrac{2}{\sqrt{4ac-b^2}} \tan^{-1} \dfrac{2ax+b}{\sqrt{4ac-b^2}}$	$(b^2 < 4ac)$
	$-\dfrac{2}{2ax+b}$	$(b^2 = 4ac)$
	$\dfrac{1}{\sqrt{b^2-4ac}} \log \dfrac{2ax+b-\sqrt{b^2-4ac}}{2ax+b+\sqrt{b^2-4ac}}$	$(b^2 > 4ac)$
$\dfrac{1}{\sqrt{ax^2+bx+c}}$	$\dfrac{1}{\sqrt{-a}} \sin^{-1} \dfrac{-2ax-b}{\sqrt{b^2-4ac}}$	$(a < 0)$
	$\dfrac{1}{\sqrt{a}} \log \left[2ax+b+2\sqrt{a(ax^2+ba+c)}\right]$	$(a > 0)$

This table brings up a somewhat unpleasant fact about finding antiderivatives. During this course we have studied the so-called "elementary" functions—algebraic functions, exponentials, logarithms, trigonometric functions, their inverses, and those constructed from them by algebraic processes and by composition. We know how to find the derivative of each such function and it is in every case an elementary function. The unpleasant fact in question is that many elementary functions do not have elementary antiderivatives, and we do not know any systematic way of finding the antiderivative of even those elementary functions which happen to have elementary antiderivatives. (An important example of an elementary function f which does not have an elementary antiderivative is defined by $f(x) = e^{x^2}$.) There are available several books which tabulate known antiderivatives, but people who use antiderivatives in practice generally use infinite series to solve their problems rather than these tables. For instance, since e^{x^2} is represented by

$$1+x^2+\frac{(x^2)^2}{2!}+\cdots+\frac{(x^2)^n}{n!}+\cdots,$$

its antiderivative is represented by

$$C+x+\frac{x^3}{3}+\cdots+\frac{x^{2n+1}}{(2n+1)n!}+\cdots.$$

The fact that the function represented by this latter series is not elementary does not seriously stand in the way of its study.

Exercises

1. (Calculation of π) Use the binomial theorem to find the MacLaurin series for $(1+x^2)^{-1}$, integrate the resulting series term by term to find the MacLaurin series for $\tan^{-1}$, and then use the fact that $\tan \pi/2 = 1$ to infer that $\pi/4 = 8(1-\frac{1}{3}+\frac{1}{5}-\frac{1}{7}+\cdots)$. Use the alternating series test to estimate the number of terms of this series needed to compute $\pi/4$ with an error less than 0.01.

2. If a function whose antiderivative is sought can be regarded as a product $(h \circ g)g'$, then the problem of finding its antiderivatve is reduced to finding an antiderivative of h. In fact, if $w' = h$, then $(w \circ g)' = (h \circ g)g'$. For instance, to evaluate $\int xe^{x^2}$ let $h(x)$ be $(\frac{1}{2})e^x$ and $g(x)$ be x^2. Since $(\frac{1}{2} \exp)'(x) = \frac{1}{2}e^x$, it follows that $((\frac{1}{2} \exp) \circ x^2)' = xe^{x^2}$. Apply this method to evaluate the following:

(a) $\int (2x+1)(x^2+x)^{10}$

(b) $\int x\sqrt{1-x^2}$

(c) $\int x \cos (x^2)$

(d) $\int x^2 \sin (x^3)$

(e) $\int \cos x \, (\sin x)^{10}$

(f) $\int \frac{(\log x)^{15}}{x}$

(g) $\int \frac{(\sin^{-1} x)^3}{\sqrt{1-x^2}}$

(h) $\int \frac{\tan^{-1} x}{1+x^2}$

(i) $\int \tan x$

3. (Integration by parts)   From the formula $(uv)' = uv' + u'v$, we deduce that $\int uv' = uv - \int u'v$. Sometimes this relation is helpful in finding antiderivatives. For instance, to evaluate $\int x \cos x$ we regard x as u and $\sin x$ as v. Then we have

$$\int x \cos x = x \sin x - \int \cos x = x \sin x - \sin x.$$

Use integration by parts to evaluate the following integrals.

(a) $\int x \sin x$

(d) $\int \tan^{-1} x$

[Hint: $u = \tan^{-1} x,\ v = x$]

(b) $\int xe^x$

(e) $\int \cos^{-1} x$

(c) $\int \log x$

(f) $\int x \sin ax$

[Hint: $u = \log x,\ v = x$]

4. Find an antiderivative of each of the following:

(a) $\dfrac{x}{ax+b}$

(e) $\dfrac{1}{x(ax+b)}$

(b) $\dfrac{x^2}{ax+b}$

(f) $\dfrac{x}{x^2+1}$

(c) $\dfrac{x}{(ax+b)^2}$

(g) $\dfrac{x^2}{x^2+1}$

(d) $\dfrac{x^2}{(ax+b)^2}$

(h) $\dfrac{x}{(x^2+1)^2}$

5. Verify the following:

(a) $\int \sqrt{x^2 \pm a^2} = \frac{1}{2}(x\sqrt{x^2 \pm a^2} \pm a^2 \log(x + \sqrt{x^2 \pm a^2}))$

(b) $\int \sqrt{a^2 - x^2} = \frac{1}{2}(x\sqrt{a^2 - x^2} + a^2 \sin^{-1}(x/a))$

(c) $\int x(x^2 - a^2)^r = \dfrac{(x^2 - a^2)^{r+1}}{2r+2},$ if $r \neq -1$

Angle Measure and the Trigonometric Functions of Angles

Trigonometric functions have important relations to angles, circles, and other geometric and trigonometric objects, but their definitions in terms of series does not make these relations apparent. In order to supply the missing connections we need some facts from the domain of geometry and trigonometry.

We need a rectangular coordinate system for our plane. Relative to this coordinate system each point has for coordinates some ordered pair (x, y) of numbers, and the distance between the points with coordinates (x_1, y_1) and (x_2, y_2) is $\sqrt{(x_1 - x_2)^2 + (y_1 - y_2)^2}$. A figure (set of points) consisting of the points of two rays with common vertex is called an *angle*. An *oriented angle* is an ordered pair of rays with a common vertex, the first ray being the *initial* side, the second ray its *terminal* side. Two oriented angles are *equivalent* if their associated point sets (angle) are congruent and if they have the same orientation. (This means that if one of the two equivalent oriented angles is slid rigidly in the plane so that its initial side coincides with that of the other, so will its terminal

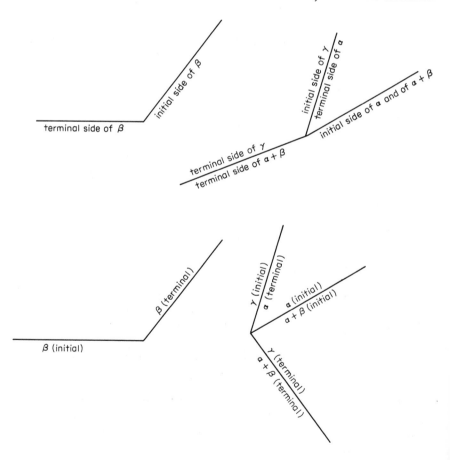

side. It is not easy to make this concept mathematically precise, and the property of the plane involved, its *orientability*, is not generally studied in elementary mathematics.)

If α and β are oriented angles, there is one and only one oriented angle γ, equivalent to β, whose initial side is the terminal side of α. The oriented angle whose initial side is the initial side of α and whose terminal side is that of γ is called the *sum* of α and β, and it is denoted by $\alpha + \beta$.

If α and α' are equivalent, and if β and β' are equivalent, so are $\alpha+\beta$ and $\alpha'+\beta'$.

If α is an angle in standard position, there is one and only one point on its terminal side whose distance from the origin is 1. If (x, y) are the coordinates of this point, we say that $x = \text{COS } \alpha$ and $y = \text{SIN } \alpha$. If α is an oriented angle not in standard position, then we say that $\text{COS } \alpha = \text{COS } \alpha'$ and $\text{SIN } \alpha = \text{SIN } \alpha'$, where α' is the angle in standard position equivalent to α'. Oriented angles α and β are equivalent if and only if $\text{COS } \alpha = \text{COS } \beta$ and $\text{SIN } \alpha = \text{SIN } \beta$.

We relate these functions SIN and COS, each of whose domains is the set of all oriented angles in the plane, to the functions sin and cos, each of whose domains is the set of all real numbers. The connection is made via lengths of circular arcs, as computed according to the formula of page 69.

LEMMA 7-30:   If C is the circle with center $(0, 0)$ and radius r, and if $(a, \sqrt{r^2-a^2})$, $(b, \sqrt{r^2-b^2})$ are two points of C with $a < b$, then the length of the minor arc connecting these points is

$$r \cos^{-1}(a/r) - r \cos^{-1}(b/r).$$

Proof: The portion of C in the upper half plane of the x-axis is the graph of f, where $f(x) = \sqrt{r^2-x^2}$. Since $f'(x) = -x/\sqrt{r^2-x^2}$, we have $\sqrt{1+f'(x)^2} = r/\sqrt{r^2-x^2}$. We know from Theorem 7-7 that if $g(x) = -r \cos^{-1}(x/r)$, then $g'(x) = r/\sqrt{r^2-x^2}$. We infer from Corollary 4-12 that the arc length in question is $r \cos^{-1}(a/r) - r \cos^{-1}(b/r)$.

COROLLARY 7-31:   The length of a semicircle is πr.

COROLLARY 7-32:   The length of the minor arc from $(a, -\sqrt{r^2-a^2})$ to $(b, -\sqrt{r^2-b^2})$, with $a < b$, is $r \cos^{-1}(a/r) - r \cos^{-1}(b/r)$.

DEFINITIONS: Let α be an oriented angle in standard position. The *principal radian measure* of α is

(a)   the length of the minor arc intercepted by α on the circle, center the origin, radius 1, if the terminal side of α is in the upper half plane of the x-axis;

(b) 2π minus the length of this arc, if the terminal side of α is in the lower half plane.

If α is not in standard position then its principal radian measure is that of the angle in standard position to which it is equivalent.

THEOREM 7-33:   Let $m(\alpha)$ be the principal radian measure of the oriented angle α. Then SIN $\alpha = \sin(m(\alpha))$, COS $\alpha = \cos(m(\alpha))$.

Proof: According to the definition of $m(\alpha)$ and Lemma 7-30, we have $m(\alpha) = \cos^{-1} a$ for angles in the upper half plane and $m(\alpha) = 2\pi - \cos^{-1} a$ for angles in the lower half plane. Since a is COS α, we see that for the upper half plane case

$$\cos m(\alpha) = \cos \cos^{-1} \text{COS } \alpha = \text{COS } \alpha$$

and for the lower half plane case

$$\cos m(\alpha) = \cos(2\pi - \cos^{-1} \text{COS } \alpha)$$
$$= 1 \cdot \text{COS } \alpha - 0$$
$$= \text{COS } \alpha.$$

Since $\sin^2 = 1 - \cos^1$ and $\text{SIN}^2 = 1 - \text{COS}^2$, the result concerning cos and COS implies that $\sin m(\alpha) = \pm\text{SIN } \alpha$. Thus to verify that $\sin m(\alpha) = \text{SIN } \alpha$ it is necessary only to verify that they have the same sign. In the upper half plane case,

$$\text{SIN } \alpha = \sqrt{1 - \text{COS}^2 \alpha} \geq 0 \qquad \text{and} \qquad 0 \leq m(\alpha) \leq \pi,$$

so $\sin(m(\alpha)) \geq 0$. In the lower half plane case,

$$\text{SIN } \alpha = \sqrt{1 - \text{COS}^2 \alpha} \leq 0 \qquad \text{and} \qquad \alpha \leq m(\alpha) \leq 2\pi,$$

so $\sin(m(\alpha)) \leq 0$.

DEFINITION: If α is an oriented angle and $m(\alpha)$ is its principal radian measure, then each of the numbers

$$m(\alpha), \quad m(\alpha) \pm 2\pi, \quad m(\alpha) \pm 4\pi, \ldots, m(\alpha) \pm 2n\pi, \ldots$$

is a *radian measure* of α.

THEOREM 7-34: Every number is a radian measure of an oriented angle, and the number x is a radian measure of the oriented angle α if and only if $\sin x = \text{SIN } \alpha$ and $\cos x = \text{COS } \alpha$.

Proof: Let α' be the angle in standard position whose terminal side contains $(\cos x, \sin x)$. Then, since $\cos^2 x + \sin^2 x = 1$, we have $\text{COS } \alpha' = \cos x$, $\text{SIN } \alpha' = \sin x$. We also have $\text{COS } \alpha' = \cos m(\alpha')$, $\text{SIN } \alpha' = \sin m(\alpha')$, where $m(\alpha')$ is the principal measure of α'. By Theorem 7-26 it is known that $\cos x = \cos m(\alpha')$, $\sin x = \sin m(\alpha')$, if and only if $x = m(\alpha') + 2n\pi$. We infer that x is a radian measure of α'. It is a radian measure of α if and only if α and α' have the same principal radian measure. This is so if and only if α and α' are equivalent, that is, if and only if $\text{SIN } \alpha = \text{SIN } \alpha'$ and $\text{COS } \alpha = \text{COS } \alpha'$.

COROLLARY 7-35: Two oriented angles are equivalent if and only if they have the same radian measures.

THEOREM 7-36: If x is a radian measure of α and if y is a radian measure of β, then $x+y$ is a radian measure of $\alpha+\beta$.

Proof: Theorem 7-34 implies that $\sin x = \text{SIN } \alpha$, $\cos c = \text{COS } \alpha$, $\sin y = \text{SIN } \beta$, $\cos y = \text{COS } \beta$. We infer from the formulas on page 123 that $\sin (x+y) = \text{SIN } (a+\beta)$ and that $\cos(x+y) = \text{COS } (\alpha+\beta)$. Our conclusion follows by applying Theorem 7-34 to $x+y$ and $\alpha+\beta$.

Exercises

1. (a) Formulate a definition of *principal degree measure* of an oriented angle, analogous to that of principal radian measure.

   (b) What should it mean to say that the number x is a degree measure of an oriented angle?

   (c) For each real number x let $d(x)$ be the oriented angle in standard position whose degree measure is x. Find $(\text{SIN} \circ d)'$ and $(\text{COS} \circ d)'$.

2. Let β be any oriented angle other than a null angle and a straight angle.

   (a) Formulate a definition of *principal β measure* for oriented angles and say what it should mean to say that the number x is the β measure of an oriented angle.

(b) If $b(x)$ is the oriented angle in standard position whose β measure is x, find $(\text{SIN} \circ b)'$ and $(\text{COS} \circ b)'$.

3. (Polar coordinates) Every function f determines a curve whose parametric equations are $x = f(t) \cos t,\ y = f(t) \sin t$. Given that f is nonnegative, verify the following statement.

(a) The distance from the origin to $P = (f(t) \cos t, f(t) \sin t)$ is $f(t)$.

(b) The oriented angle whose initial side is the x-axis and whose terminal side is the ray from the origin to P has radian measure t (provided that P is not the origin).

(c) $f(t) = x^2 + y^2$, $\tan t = y/x$ at P.

(d) the tangent to the curve at P has slope

$$\frac{f'(t) \sin t + f(t) \cos t}{f'(t) \cos t - f(t) \sin t}.$$

(e) The length of the arc between points corresponding to t_1 and t_2 is

$$\int_{t_1}^{t_2} \sqrt{f(t)^2 + f'(t)^2}.$$

Check this formula by using it to find the length of a circular arc on the circle whose parametric equations are $x = R \cos t$, $= R \sin t$.

Curvature and the Osculating Circle

No line is straighter than any other line, nor is a line straighter at one of its points than at another. For curves the situation is more complicated. It can be maintained that some curves have greater curvature than others and that on some curves the curvature changes from point to point. For instance, the curve shown in this figure surely has greater curvature at A than at B.

We are going to introduce a precise numerical measurement for curvature. To do so we observe that at each of its points a curve has a direction, namely, the direction of its tangent at that point, and that the rate at which this direction changes as the curve is traced out is an index of the curvature of the curve. The following definition expresses this observation formally, using the inclination of the tangent line to a curve at a point as an indicator of the direction of the curve at that point.

DEFINITION: Let G be the graph of the function f. For each point $(x, f(x))$ of G let $G(x)$ be the measure of the inclination of the tangent to G at that point, and let $s(x)$ be the length of the arc length of G, measured from some given point P_0 to $(x, f(x))$. Then the *curvature of G at* $(x, f(x))$ is the absolute value of the rate of change of θ with respect to s.

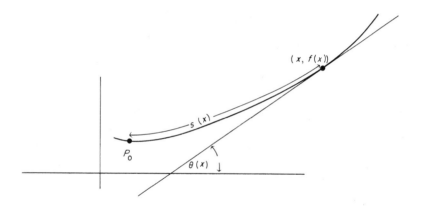

THEOREM 7:37:   If G is the graph of the function f, then the curvature of G at $(x, f(x))$ is

$$\left| \frac{f''(x)}{(1+f'(x)^2)^{3/2}} \right|.$$

Proof: We have $\tan(\theta(x)) = f'(x)$, so $\theta(x) = \tan^{-1}(f'(x))$. We know that the rate of change of θ with respect to s at x is $\theta'(x)/s'(x)$. Since $\theta'(x)$ is $f''(x)/(1 + f'(x)^2)$ and since $s'(x)$ is $(1 + f'(x)^2)^{1/2}$, the conclusion follows.

Our next examples show that the curvature formula gives credible results when it is applied to lines and circles.

Examples:

(a) A line is the graph of $f(x) = mx + b$. We have $f''(x) = 0$ for every x, whence the curvature of the line is zero at each of its points.

(b)   A circle is not actually the graph of a function, but its upper and lower halves are. Let G be the circle whose center is (a, b) and whose radius is r. Then each point (x, y) on G satisfies $(x - a)^2 + (y - b)^2 = r^2$. The upper half of G is therefore the graph of $f(x) = b + (r^2 - (x - a)^2)^{1/2}$. We compute

$$f'(x) = -(x - a)(r^2 - (x - a)^2)^{-1/2}$$

$$f''(x) = -r^2(r^2 - (x - a)^2)^{-3/2}$$

$$1 + f'(x)^2 = r^2(r^2 - (x - a)^2)^{-1}$$

$$\frac{f''(x)}{(1 + f'(x)^2)^{3/2}} = \frac{1}{r}.$$

The lower half of G is the graph of $f(x) = b - (r^2 - (x - a)^2)^{1/2}$. A similar calculation shows that at each of its points its curvature is also $1/r$. We conclude that a circle of radius r has curvature $1/r$ at each of its points.

Let G be the graph of the function f and let P be a point of G. We have seen that, of all lines through P, the tangent line provides the best approximation to G at P. We now consider circles through P and seek the circle which provides the best approximation to G at P. It is reasonable to confine the search to circles whose tangent at P is the same as the tangent to G at P.

Note: If the curvature of a curve C at P is not zero, then, near P, C lies wholly on one side of its tangent at P.

DEFINITION: Let P be a point on the curve G at which the curvature k is not zero. The *osculating circle to G at P* is the circle through P whose tangent at P is the tangent to G at P, whose radius is $1/k$, and which lies on the same side of this tangent as P does.

THEOREM 7-38:   The osculating circle to the curve G at point P is closer to G near P than any other circle.

Proof: We introduce a new rectangular coordinate system whose origin is P and whose x-axis is the tangent to G at P. This changes neither the curvature nor the osculating circle. Then each of the circles being considered is specified by a number q; it has center $(0, q)$ and radius $|q|$. Its equation is $x^2 + (y - q)^2 = q^2$. The upper half of this circle is the graph of $h(x) = q + (q^2 - x^2)^{1/2}$ and the lower half is the graph of $h(x) = q - (q^2 - x^2)^{1/2}$. Since it is the latter which passes through the origin, we work with it. The problem reduces to choosing q so as to make the difference between $f(x)$ and $h(x)$ as small as possible. Recalling that $f(0) = f'(0) = 0)$, we have

$$f(x) = \frac{f''(0)}{2!} x^2 + \frac{f'''(0)}{3!} x^3 + \cdots .$$

Let us expand $h(x)$ into a series. The binomial theorem gives us, for $(q^2 - x^2)^{1/2}$, the representation $q(1 - \frac{1}{2}(x^2/q^2) + \cdots)$, so the expression for $h(x)$ is $\frac{1}{2}(x^2/q) + \cdots$. It follows that the difference in question has order one for every choice of q except $1/f''(0)$ and has order at least two for this value of q. We infer that the circle with center $(0, 1/f''(0))$ and radius $|1/f''(0)|$ provides a better approximation to G near $(0, 0)$ than that of any other circle. We check to see if the circle singled out is actually the osculating circle. Our formula for curvature gives $|f''(0)|$ as the curvature of G at $(0, 0)$, so our circle has the correct radius. To see that it lies on the same side of the x-axis as G does, observe that $f(x)$ has the same sign as $f''(0)$ near $(0, 0)$ and that the same is true for $h(x)$, when $q = 1/f''(0)$.

Exercises

1. Find the value at x of the curvature of the parabola $y = x^2$. Show that the maximum curvature occurs at $(0, 0)$ and that the curvature diminishes as the tracing point recedes from this point. Relate the shape of the parabola to this observation.

2. (a) Show that if a curve has parametric equations $x = f(t), y = g(t)$, then its curvature at t is

$$\frac{|f'(t)g''(t) - g'(t)f''(t)|}{(f'(t)^2 + g'(t)^2)^{3/2}}$$

(b) Use this formula to compute the curvature of the circle $x = a + r \cos t, y = b + r \sin t$.

3. Show that if a curve has zero curvature at each of its points, then it is a part of a line.

4. Let k be a nonzero number. Show that if a curve has curvature k at each of its points, then it is part of a circle of radius $1/k$.

5. Let two rectangular coordinate systems with the same unit length be selected in the plane. Suppose curve G is the graph of function f relative to the first system and is the graph of f^* relative to the second. Let k be the value of the curvature formula, evaluated using f, and let k^* be the value of the curvature formula, evaluated using f^*. Prove that $k = k^*$ for each point of G.

6. (Order of contact)   Let f_1 and f_2 be functions whose graphs G_1 and G_2 intersect at (a, b). We say that G_1 and G_2 have *contact of order n at (a, b)* if $f_1 - f_2$ has order n at a. Prove the following:

   (a)   If G_2 is a line, then G_1 and G_2 have contact of order at least one at (a, b) if and only if G_2 is the tangent to G_1 at that point.

   (b)   The order of contact of G_1 and its tangent at (a, b) exceeds one if and only if $f''(a) = 0$.

   (c)   An *inflection point* on a curve is one at which f'' has the value zero. Prove that at such a point there is no best approximating circle.

Some Peculiarities
of Infinite Series

The sum representation $a_0+a_1+a_2+\cdots$ for infinite series is a little misleading. It invites the unwary to perform apparently harmless manipulations which can lead to incorrect conclusions. For finite sums $a_0+a_1+\cdots+a_n$, if one rearranges the order of the terms, or groups them by means of parentheses, the new sum so obtained is equal to the original. For infinite series this is not so.

Consider, for instance, the infinite series

$$1-\frac{1}{2}+\frac{1}{3}-\cdots+\frac{(-1)^{n+1}}{n}+\cdots.$$

This series converges to log 2. If a is any number whatsoever, this infinite series can be rearranged so that the resulting infinite series converges to a. It can also be rearranged so that the resulting series diverges. There is nothing particularly shocking about this if the activities in question are stated with reference to the term sequence and partial sum sequence which make up the infinite series. The act of rearranging the terms of the given infinite series is then seen as the replacement of one term sequence by a quite different one, and the fact that it can have a quite different limit is not surprising.

The insertion of parentheses into infinite series can also involve essential change. For instance, the divergent infinite series $1-1+1-1+\cdots$ is converted into the convergent infinite series $0+0+0+\cdots$ by insertion of parentheses $(1-1)+(1-1)+(1-1)+\cdots$. Grouping the terms of an infinite series in this way yields a new infinite series whose partial sum sequence is actually a subsequence of that of the original. Therefore, if the partial sum sequence of the original infinite series has limit a, so must the partial sum sequence of the new infinite series. This implies that if the original infinite series has sum a, so does the infinite

143

series obtained from it by grouping its terms. However, as the example $1-1+1-1+\cdots$ shows, inserting parentheses into a divergent infinite series can produce a convergent infinite series.

The product of power series is another subject in which the unexpected can happen. The power series $1-(1/\sqrt{2})x+(1/\sqrt{3})x^2-\cdots$ converges for $x=1$, but its square does not. On the other hand, neither of the power series $2+2x+2^2x^2+\cdots+2^nx^n+\cdots$ and $-1+x+x^2+\cdots+x^2+\cdots$ converges for $x=1$, but their product $-2+0\cdot x^1+0\cdot x^2+\cdots+0\cdot x^n+\cdots$ converges for every x.

The representation of functions as sum functions of power series also leads to some anomolies. One that we have already noticed concerns the failure of a MacLaurin series to represent the function of which it is the expansion. For instance, if $f(x)=(1-x)^{-1}$ for $x\neq 1$, then the series $\sum x^n$ converges to $f(x)$ if $|x|<1$, but does not converge at all at the other values in the domain of f. A more extreme example of the failure of a MacLaurin series to represent the function of which it is the expansion is exhibited by the function for which $f(x)=\exp(-1/x^2)$. This function has the property that $0=f(0)=f'(0)=\cdots=f^{(n)}(0)$ $=\cdots$, and thus the MacLaurin series for this function is $0+0x+0x^2$ $+\cdots$. While this series converges for every x, it only converges to $f(x)$ at $x=0$.

These examples and many others of a similar nature are discussed in Gelbaum and Olmsted, *Counterexamples in Analysis*, Holden-Day, 1964.

Other Notations for the
Derivative and Differential

The derivative of a function is itself a function and is entitled to a name of its own. It is customary to give the derivative a name that indicates both the function from which it was derived and the fact that it was derived by differentiation. Our practice has been to use f' for the derivative of f, to use sin' for the derivative of sin, to use log' for the derivative of log, etc. For functions to which no name has been attached (for instance, the function whose value at x is x^n), this procedure is not available.

There are other procedures in general use for naming derivatives. One of them denotes $f, f', f'', \ldots, f^{(n)}, \ldots$ by $f, Df, D^2f, \ldots, D^{(n)}f, \ldots$. Perhaps the most frequently met expression in this part of the mathematical world is $\frac{dy}{dx}$. There are certain conventions about its use in naming derivatives which need to be made explicit. It is used where x and y are both connected with sets, and its use assumes that there is under discussion some unique function from the x set to the y set. When this is the case, $\frac{dy}{dx}$ denotes the derivative of this function. Consider, for instance, a particle moving in a plane. At each time t the particle has an x-coordinate and a y-coordinate. There are then at least two functions present, that which assigns x values to t values and that which assigns y values to t values. Call the first f and the second g. Then, in this d notation, $\frac{dx}{dt}$ is f' and $\frac{dy}{dt}$ is g'. What about $\frac{dy}{dx}$ in this situation? The only available function from the x set to the y set is $g \circ f^{-1}$. The expression $\frac{dy}{dx}$ means the derivative of this function, that is, $(g \circ f^{-1})'$. The notation $\dfrac{dy}{dx}$ could cause trouble if there were under discussion several different functions from the x set to the y set. When this is the case the notation should be avoided. The procedure uses $\dfrac{d^2y}{dx^2}, \ldots \dfrac{d^ny}{dx^n}, \ldots$ for higher derivatives.

Another notation, which goes back to Newton and is used mainly by physicists, employs dots in such a way that $\dot{x}, \dot{y}, \dot{w}$, denote derivatives. This notation is confined to situations in which there is a unique function from time values to x values (or to y values, or to w values) and $\dot{x}$ (or $\dot{y}$ or $\dot{w}$) means the derivative of this function. Second derivatives are denoted by two dots, and third derivatives by three, as in $\dddot{x}$ and $\dddot{y}$. For obvious reasons this notation does not extend to n-th derivatives for large n.

The student will meet differentials in his later mathematical work and needs a few facts to prepare himself for that encounter. We have not used the term "differential" in this course, but differentials themselves have been present. Let f be a function and let $f(t) + f'(t)(x-t)$ be its $(t, 1)$ approximation. Then the function whose value at (x, t) is $f'(t)(x-t)$ is the *differential of f at* (x, t). It is, in effect, the function defined by the $(t, 1)$ approximation to $f - f(t)$. The change or increment $f(x) - f(t)$ is often denoted by Δf, and the differential by df. We see that dy is an approximation to Δf of precisely the type we have studied so extensively.

The Riemann Integral

In contemporary calculus courses a considerable amount of time is devoted to the Riemann integral. This integral also appears frequently in mathematical literature. Therefore, even though the author believes that its presence in elementary mathematics is a needless complication, he believes that some description of it is needed for the students of this course. The following definitions and theorem set forth its major properties.

DEFINITIONS: A *subdivision* of the closed interval $[a, b]$ is a finite set of numbers $x_1, x_2, \ldots, x_n$ for which $a < x_1 < x_2 < \cdots < x_n < b$. The *norm* of a subdivision is the maximum of x_1-a, x_2-x_1, $\cdots$, $b-x_n$. Let f be a function whose domain includes $[a, b]$. An *approximating sum* for the pair f, $[a, b]$ is a number obtained by choosing a subdivision of $[a, b]$, choosing a number t_1 in $[x_1, a]$, a number t_2 in $[x_2, x_1], \ldots$, a number t_{n+1} in $[x_n, b]$ and evaluating

$$f(t_1)(x_1-a)+f(t_2)(x_2-x_1)+\cdots+f(t_{n+1})(b-x_n).$$

The function f is said to be *integrable* on $[a, b]$ if there is a number I such that, for each positive number e, there is a positive number d such that $|I-S| < e$ for every approximating sum S that arises from a subdivision of norm less than d. If this number I exists, it is denoted by $\int_a^b f(x)\, dx$ and is called the "integral of f over $[a, b]$," the "definite integral of f over $[a, b]$," and the "Riemann integral of f over $[a, b]$."

The importance of the Riemann integral has been that it provides a formula for the value of many important quantities of pure and applied mathematics. The number I is specified in an extremely complicated way, but is found in a relatively simple way in most of the important cases of elementary mathematics, thanks to the following theorem:

THEOREM (Fundamental Theorem of Integral Calculus): If f is continuous on $[a, b]$, then there is a differentiable function F such that

$$F' = f \quad \text{and} \quad \int_a^b f(x)\, dx = F(b) - F(a).$$

This theorem implies that the integral exists and also gives an important hint as to how to find it: by referring the whole matter to a search for antiderivatives, without further reference to the approximating sums. The approximating sums do not disappear from the scene completely; they survive as approximations to those integrals whose exact values cannot be found.

Answers and Comments
for Selected Exercises

Page 3
1. (a) $|x| < 2$ (d) $|x - \frac{1}{2}| \leq \frac{17}{2}$
2. (c) $(-2, 4)$ (e) $[-5, -1]$
3. (b) $|a| = -a$, $|b| = -b$, $|a+b| = -(a+b) = |a| + |b|$
4. (a) 0 is between a and b.

Page 4
1.   5 $-\frac{1}{2}$ 5
    -15 21   5
    -50 10   15

Page 7
1. (a) $0, 1, 4, 9, 16$ (c) $2, 0, 2, 0, 2$ (f) $0, 1, 5, 14, 30$
2. $a_0 = 6$, $a_n = a_0 + a_1 + \cdots + a_{n-1}$, $n = 1, 2, 3, \ldots$
3. $a_n = b_n c_n$, $n = 0, 1, 2, \ldots$ 7. (a) $1, 2, 4, 8, \ldots, 2^n, \ldots$
9. (a) $1^3 + 2^3 + \cdots + n^3$ (b) $\sum_{i=1}^{n} i$

Page 12
2. (d) $1 - x^{n+1}$
5. If $AB = 0$, then it has no degree. If neither A nor B were 0, then their product would have as degree the sum of those of A and B.
7. (g) $x^9 + 3x^6 y^2 + 3x^3 y^4 + y^6$ 8. Expand $(1+1)^n$.   9. Expand $(1-1)^n$.
14. (a) Quotient $4 + 5x$, remainder 3   (b) Quotient 5, remainder $3 + 4x$
    (c) and (d) Quotient 0, remainder $3 + 4x + 5x^2$
15. (a) Quotient $4 + 5(x-1)$, remainder 3
    (b) Quotient 5, remainder $3 + 4(x-1)$
    (c) and (d) Quotient 0, remainder $3 + 4(x-1) + 5(x-1)^2$

Page 18
1. (a) 1,   (h) $-3 - 2x^2 - 3x^4$
4. (a) $A(x) = cx$,   (b) x^n

6. (a) and (b) $-\dfrac{a}{b} + \dfrac{x}{b}$

8. Let $t_2 = t_4 = 0$, $t_3 = 1$. Then $A(t_1) = (A(1) - A(0))t_1 + A(0)$, for every t_1, so A is defined by $(A(1) - A(0))x + A(0)$.

10. The equation $P(x) = c$ has at most n roots.

Page 22

1. (a) $n+1$ (b) $\dfrac{n(n+1)}{2}$ (c) $\dfrac{n(n^2+1)}{2}$

3. Let $P(n)$ be the polynomial formula for a_n and let $Q(n)$ be the polynomial formula for b_n. Then $P(n) + Q(n)$ and $P(n)Q(n)$ are polynomial formulas for $a_n + b_n$ and $a_n b_n$, respectively.

5. Let $P(n)$ be the polynomial formula for a_n.
    (a) The polynomial formula for a_{2n} is $P(2n)$.
    (b) The polynomial formula for a_{n^2} is $P(n^2)$.
    (c) The polynomial formula for a_{n^3} is $P(n^3)$.

Page 27

1. (a) $1+2x$ (c) $7+11(x-1)$ (f) $1-(x+1)$
    (b) $1+2x+3x^2$ (e) $1-(x+1)$

2. The accuracy improves as x approaches t and as n increases.

3. $1+x^2$, $1-(x-1)^2$

5. $\frac{1}{3}+\frac{4}{9}x$, $\frac{1}{7}+\frac{4}{49}(x+1)$

10. (a) $t+(x-t)$, $t^2+2t(x-t)$, $t^3+3t^2(x-t)$, $t^n+nt^{n-1}(x-t)$

Page 31

1. (a) $A(x) = \frac{1}{2}+\frac{1}{4}x$ (c) $A(x) = \frac{1}{4}+\frac{1}{2}x$
    (b) $A(x) = 2-3x+2x^2$ (d) $A(x) = 1-\frac{1}{3}(x+1)+\frac{2}{27}(x+1)$.

4. (a) $2+\frac{1}{4}(x-4)$ (c) $2+\frac{1}{4}(x-4)-\frac{1}{64}(x-4)^2$
    (b) $-2-\frac{1}{4}(x-4)$ (d) $-2-\frac{1}{4}(x-4)+\frac{1}{64}(x-4)^2$

6. $(0, 1)$ square root of $1+2x$ is $1+x$, $(0, 1)$ reciprocal of $1+x$ is $1-x$, $(0, 1)$ reciprocal of $1+2x$ is $1-2x$, $(0, 1)$ square root of $1-2x$ is $1-x$.

Page 37

2. Part (1). If $|f| \geq |g|$ for $|x-t| \leq d_1$ and if $|g| \geq |h|$ for $|x-t| \leq d_2$, then $|f| \geq |h|$ for $|x-t| \leq d^*$, where d^* is the smaller of d_1 and d_2.
    Part (3). If $|f_1| \geq |g_1|$ for $|x-t| \leq d_1$ and if $|f_2| \geq |g_2|$ for $|x-t| \leq d_2$, then $|f_1 f_2| \geq |g_1 g_2|$ for $|x-t| \leq d^*$, where d^* is the smaller of d_1 and d_2.

3. (a) $A(x) = B(x) + 2x^2$. If $x > 0$, then $|A(x)| > |B(x)|$, but if x is small and negative, then $0 > A(x) > B(x)$ and $|B(x)| > |A(x)|$.
    (b) $A(x) = B(x) + 2x^3$. If $x > 0$, then $A(x) > B(x) > 0$, so $|A(x)| > |B(x)|$. If $x < 0$, then $0 > B(x) > A(x)$ and $|A(x)| > |B(x)|$ again.

4. There must be an r for which $a_0 = a_1 = \cdots = a_r = b_0 = b_1 = \cdots = b_r = 0$, with $a_{r+1} \neq 0$ and $|a_{r+1}| = |b_{r+1}|$. If not, then, according to Theorem 3-4, one would dominate the other. Even this condition does not prevent this from occurring.

Page 42

1. $a+bt+b(x-t)$ for P, $c+dt+d(x-t)$ for Q, $a+bt+c+dt+(b+d)(x-t)$ for $P+Q$,

   $(a+bt)(c+dt) + (d(a+bt) + b(c+dt)(x-t))$ for PQ, $\dfrac{1}{c+dt} - \dfrac{d}{(c+dt)^2}(x-t)$,

   $c+dt \neq 0$, for $1/Q$, $\dfrac{a+bt}{c+dt} + \dfrac{b(c+dt) - d(a+bt)}{(c+dt)^2}(x-t)$ for P/Q, $(a+bt)^r + r$

   $(a+bt)^{r-1}b(x-t)$ for P^r,

2.   (a) $1+x$, $1-x$, $\frac{1}{3}+\frac{2}{9}x$

3.   (a)   0   (c) $1+2(x-1)$ (e) $1-2(x+1)$
     (b) x^2 (d) x^2 (f) x^2

5.   (c)   If $P(x)$ is the $(t, 1)$ approximation to f, then the $(t, 1)$ square of $P(x)$ is the $(t, 1)$ approximation to $1+x$, so $P(x)$ is a $(t, 1)$ square root of $1+x$: There are two but only the one proposed has positive values near t.

8.   Since $|f(t)| \leq 1$ for every t, f is bounded at every t. Since in every interval there are rational and irrational numbers, we cannot have $|f(x)-f(t)| < 1$ throughout any interval.

12.   (a) $1+2x$ (c) $4+4(x-1)$ (e) $3+3(x-1)+4(x-1)^2$
      (b)   1   (d) $2+2(x-1)$ (f) $1+9(x-1)+36(x-1)^2$
      (g) $\sum_{n=0}^{i} \binom{rs}{i} t^{rs-i}(x-t)^i$

14.   (c) $1+\frac{1}{4}x$ (h) $1-\frac{1}{4}x$

16.   (a) $x-1$ (b) $x-1$ (c) $(x-1)-(x-1)^2$
      (g) $x-\dfrac{x^2}{2}+\dfrac{x^2}{3}-\cdots+\dfrac{(-1)^n x^n}{n+1}$

Page 48

1.   No, because the domain in question is not a closed interval.

3.   There is a positive number e such that every interval $[t-d, t+d]$ contains an x for which $|f(x)-f(t)| > e$.

7.   They are all compositions of functions known to be continuous.

Page 53

2.   (a) $3+8x$ (c) $4(2+3x+4x^2)^3(3+8x)$
     (b) $(3+8x)/(2+3x+4x^2)^2$ (d) $\frac{1}{4}(2+3x+4x^2)^{-3/4}(3+8x)$

6.   (a) $a_0 x+\dfrac{a_1}{2}x^2+\dfrac{a_2}{3}x^3+\cdots+\dfrac{a_n}{n+1}x^{n+1}$

7.   (e) $\frac{2}{3}, 2, \frac{2}{3}, -\frac{1}{2}$

Page 59

1.   (a) $y=1+2(x-1)$ (c) $y=7+4(x-1)$ (e) $y=1-\frac{3}{2}(x-1)$
     (b) $y=7+8(x-1)$ (d) $y=3$

3.   25

6.   (a) $\left|\dfrac{am}{\sqrt{1+m^2}}\right|$ (b) $|\sqrt{a^2+b^2}-1|$

Page 64

1.   (a) $\dfrac{x^3}{3}-9$ (e) $\dfrac{(2x+3)^4}{8}-\dfrac{9^4}{8}$ (i) $\dfrac{2}{3b}(a+bx)^{3/2}-\dfrac{2}{3b}(a+3b)^{3/2}$

4.   (b) $(g \circ f^{-1})' = (g' \circ f^{-1})(f^{-1})'$. Evaluating at x, we have $(g' \circ f^{-1})(x) = g'(t)$ and $(f^{-1})'(x) = 1/f'(t)$ (Theorem 4-13).

Page 70

1.   (a) $\dfrac{3^3}{3}-\dfrac{(-1)^3}{3}$ (b) $\frac{2}{3}4^{3/2}-\frac{2}{3}$ (c) $1-1/t$

3. (a) $\displaystyle\int_{-R}^{R} 4(R^2-x^2)$ (c) $\displaystyle\int_{-R}^{R} (R^2-x^2)$

    (b) $\displaystyle\int_{-R}^{R} \sqrt{3}(R^2-x^2)$ (d) $\dfrac{\pi}{2}\displaystyle\int_{-R}^{R} (R^2-x^2)$

5. (a) $\displaystyle\int_{-1}^{3} \sqrt{1+4x^2}$ (b) $\displaystyle\int_{-1}^{3} \sqrt{1+1/(4x^2)}$ (c) $\displaystyle\int_{-1}^{3} \sqrt{1+4/x^6}$

Page 75
1. (a) $-3-8t+3t^2$ (b) $-8+6t$ (c) $4/3$ (d) $3-1/3$
3. $0,\ 2\pi$ at 0; $2\pi,\ 2\pi$ at 1; $4\pi,\ 2\pi$ at 2; $2\pi R,\ 2\pi$ at R.

Page 78
2. (b) $f(b) = a^{-4}-4a^{-5}(b-a)+10a^{-6}(b-a)^2-20a^{-7}(b-a)^3$ with an error less than $35a^{-8}(b-a)^4$ if $b > a > 0$. If $b = 11$, $a = 10$, then
    $f(11) = 0.0001-0.00004+0.00001-0.000002$
    $= 0.000068$ with error less than 0.00000035
3. $h'' = (g''\circ f^{-1})((f^{-1})')^2+(g'\circ f^{-1})(f^{-1})''$
5   (a) The slopes $(f(q)-f(p))/(q-p)$ and $(f(r)-f(q))/(r-q)$ equal $f'(c_1)$ and $f'(c_2)$, where c_1 is in the interval (q, p) and c_2 in (r, q). Since $c_1 < c_2$, we have $f(c_1) < f(c_2)$.
6. $f-f(t)$ and its (t, n) approximation $\dfrac{f^{(n)}(t)(x-t)^n}{n!}$ have the same sign near t. For this sign not to change, n must be even, and, if n is even, its sign must be that of $f^{(n)}(t)$. Conclusions: relative maximum if n even, $f^{(n)}(t) < 0$, relative minimum if n even, $f^{(n)}(t) > 0$, neither if n odd.

Page 82
1. (a) $0.33\cdots 3$ (to n places) equals $3(0.1)+3(0.1)^2+\cdots+3(0.1)^n = \dfrac{1-(0.1)^n}{3}$

    $\tfrac{1}{3}-0.33\cdots 3 = \dfrac{(0.1)^n}{3}$. If $n > 9$, this is less than $(0.1)^{10}$.
2. $|t-s| \le |t-a_n|+|a_n-s|$. If $|t-s| \ne 0$, then, for large n, $|t-a_n| < |t-s|/2$ and $|a_n-s| < |t-s|/2$, so $|t-s| < |t-s|$, a contradiction.
6. Choose an interval with center s that excludes 0 and prove that there is an N such that a_n is in that interval if $n > N$.

Page 90
1. (a) $\sum_{i=0}^{\infty} 1^i$ (b) $\sum_{i=0}^{\infty} (-1)^i$ (c) $\sum_{i=0}^{\infty} 1/3^i$ (h) $\sum_{i=0}^{\infty} (-1)^i x^{2i+1}$
    (i) Let $h(i)$ be 1 if the remainder of i after division by 4 is 0 or 1; let it be -1 otherwise. Then an answer is $\sum_{i=0}^{\infty} h(i)$.
3. Show that its partial sum sequence is a Cauchy sequence.
13. Let t be a number between 1 and s. Then, from some place N on, $|a_{N+r}| < |a_N t^r|$ if $|t| > |s|$ and $|a_{N+r}| > |a_N t^r|$ if $|t| < |s|$. In the first case $|t| < 1$; in the second, $|t| > 1$. The conclusion follows from the comparison test.

Page 95
1. (a) $a_0 x+a_1 x^3+\cdots+a_i x^{2i+1}+\cdots$ (b) $a_0+a_1 x^2+\cdots+a_i x^{2i}+\cdots$
5. $a_n = 1/n!$

6. (d) $\displaystyle\sum \frac{\left(\frac{1}{n}\right)\left(\frac{1}{n}-1\right)\cdots\left(\frac{1}{n}-i+1\right)}{i!}\cdot x^i$

13. (a) $\sum 2^i x^{i+1}$

Page 102
1. (c) $|x| < 1$ for the first two, every x for the next two, the interval $|x+5| < 1$ for the next to the last, every x for the last.

Page 109
1. (a) $1+2x+3x^2+\cdots$ (b) $x+\dfrac{x^2}{2}+\dfrac{x^3}{3}+\cdots$

3. The MacLaurin series for f is

$$\sum \frac{c^i x^i}{i!}$$

4. f and f' are continuous on every closed subinterval of the given interval, hence bounded. Since $f^{(n)}$ is either f or f', it shares their bound.

Page 112
1. (a) $a_1 = 1,\ a_2 = -1/2$
2. (a) $-x/y$
3. (b) $h = h_0 + v_0 t - \dfrac{(rv_0+g)}{2}t^2 + \dfrac{r(rv_0+g)}{6}t^3 + \cdots$

Page 116
1. (c) $\displaystyle\sum \frac{e^t(x-t)^n}{n!}$

2. (a) $\displaystyle\sum \frac{w^n x^n}{n!}$ where $a = e^w$.

4. (c) $-2xe^{-x^2}$
5. Let $10 = e^w$. (a) $w10^x$ (c) $2xw10^{x^2}$

                       (b) $2w10^x$ (d) $\dfrac{1}{2\sqrt{x}}\,w10^{\sqrt{x}}$

12. (a) Follows directly from the series.

    (b) Let x_0 be $(n+1)/a^{n+1}$; use $e^{ax} > \dfrac{(ax)^{n+1}}{(n+1)!} = \left(\dfrac{a^{n+1}x}{n+1}\right)\dfrac{x^n}{n!}$.

    (c) Let x_0 be $p(n+1)!/a^{n+1}$ and proceed as in b.

Page 121
1. (a) $2/x$ (b) $2\log x/x$ (c) $1/x$ (d) $\log 2$
    (j) $\log_b e\, f'(x)/f(x)$
3. Subtract the series for $\log(1-x)$ from that for $\log(1+x)$, divide by 2, and use $\log A - \log B = \log(A/B)$.

10. $\sum(-1)^n x^{2n}$, $\displaystyle\sum \frac{(-1)^n}{2n+1}x^{2n+1}$.

12. Refer to Exercise 12, p. 118.

Page 128

7. (a) $2\cos 2x$ (e) $3\cos(3x+4)$ (i) $2x\cos(x^2)$
    (b) $-2\sin 2x$ (f) $-a\sin(ax+b)$ (j) $-2x\sin(x^2)$

    (c) $\frac{1}{2}\cos\dfrac{x}{2}$ (g) $2\sin x\cos x$ (k) $\cos x/\sin x$

    (d) $-\frac{1}{2}\sin\dfrac{x}{2}$ (h) $-2\cos x\sin x$

8. $\tan' = 1/\cos^2,\ 0+x+0x^2+(\frac{1}{3})x^3$
9. (a) $\cot' = -1/\sin^2.$ Since $\sin 0 = 0$, cot is not defined at 0.
    (b) $\sec' = \sin/\cos^2,\ 1+0x+\frac{1}{2}x^2+0x^3$

Page 132

1. About 50 terms
2. (b) $-\frac{1}{3}(1-x^2)^{3/2}$
    (i) $\tan = \sin/\cos = -(\log' \circ \cos)\cos' = -(\log \circ \cos)'$
3. (c) $x\log x - x$
5. In each case differentiate the proposed antiderivative.

Page 137

3. (a) $\sqrt{(f(t)\cos t)^2 + (f(t)\sin t)^2} = f(t)$
    (b) Call this angle θ. Then $\text{COS}\,\theta = \cos t$ and $\text{SIN}\,\theta = \sin t$.
    (d) This is $(f(t)\sin t)'/(f(t)\cos t)'$. Compare Exercise 4(b), p. 65.

Page 140

1. $2/(1+4x^2)^{3/2}$. Decreases as x moves away from 0. Parabola flattens as point recedes from vertex.
3. If $f'' = 0$, then $f(x) = a+bx$.
4. f satisfies the equation $f'' = k(1+f'^2)^{3/2}$. Let g be the function whose graph is the osculating circle to the graph of f at some point. Then $g'' = k(1+g'^2)^{3/2}$. Therefore f and g must have the same coefficients in their Taylor expansions, whence, by the Identity Theorem, they must have the same values where they are both defined.

Index